HARNESSING THE EARTHWORM

HARNESSING THE EARTHWORM

A practical inquiry into soil-building, soil conditioning, and plant nutrition through the action of earthworms, with instructions for intensive propagation and use of Domesticated Earthworms in biological soil-building

by

THOMAS J. BARRETT

with an introduction by
E. B. BALFOUR

SHIELDS PUBLICATIONS

ELGIN, ILLINOIS 60120

ISBN 0-914116-09-6

Printed in the United States of America

CONTENTS

v

CONTENTS

ILLUSTRATIONS

Of earthworms: 'It may be doubted whether there are many other animals which have played so important a part in the history of the world as have these lowly organized creatures.'

CHARLES DARWIN

INTRODUCTION

'When the question is asked, "Can I build top-soil?" the answer is "Yes", and when the first question is followed by a second question, "How can I do it?" the answer is "Feed earthworms".' That is the last sentence of this book, and it seems to me particularly appropriate to use it as the first sentence of my introduction, because it serves equally well as a preface to, or a summary of, what the book is all about, and this fact symbolizes that in the Wheel of Life, or the Nutrition Cycle, or by whatever other name you prefer to call it, there is neither beginning nor end, but only continuity; an unbroken progression of birth, growth, reproduction, decline, death, decay, rebirth—a continuous flow of substances passing from one form of life to another, round and round the cycle without end.

Dr. Barrett puts it rather more simply; he says, 'Earthworms are soil builders, everything else—plant, animal, man and bacteria are food for earthworms whose function is to mix living matter with mineral particles and send them forth on their round once again.'

That is the cycle as established by nature and operated by the creative, i.e., living, forces. It worked on an ever-ascending spiral, accumulating yet richer and more varied life forms, until man arrived upon the scene. It has been left to this supposedly most intelligent of all creation's species to put the wheel into reverse by abandoning creative motive power in favour of consumptive power, i.e., the destructive forces. In so doing man has enacted the role of the parasite whose ravages destroy the host upon which it is dependent for sustenance. He has been guilty of this behaviour since the early dawn of 'civilization'. His host is the fertile topsoil forming the surface covering of the globe; a thin covering now, very threadbare in places. 'The Wasting Basis of Civilization', so has Sir John Boyd Orr defined soil fertility. It is man who is responsible for this wasting. Of the fertile cultivatable area of the U.S.A., as it was found by the pioneers, one-quarter has gone for ever, so their soil experts tell us, and many million acres are still disappearing annually. The same story comes from South Africa. Deserts can be seen there extending for hundreds of square miles, that were producing good crops only thirty years ago. Australia and New Zealand have the same sorry record of man's rapacious exploitation to relate, and even European soil shows signs of the same decline.

The phenomenon is not new. In the name of economic necessity, God forgive him, mankind has destroyed the source of his food since before the days when part of the Sahara Desert was known as the granary of Rome. The two new factors are the speed with which modern man can turn fertile land into desert, and the fact that there no longer exist any new virgin lands for him to discover and exploit. He has reached the last barrier. At last he must learn the bitter lesson of his past mistakes or perish from the face of the earth, like other species, now extinct, who failed to solve the problem of how to co-operate with their environment.

That is the major crisis facing the human race to-day. It is a challenge beside which, as a recent writer put it, the bickerings of Foreign Ministers sound like the jabbering on Monkey Hill.

Those of us who believe that the living, creative forces are the only ones that can promote and sustain life, know that soil fertility can still be maintained by obeying nature's law of return, and that by this means vitality in soil, plant, animal and man results, but the time is short, and mass action is required now if it is not to be too late. The warning has been cried aloud from the housetops by men of knowledge and the highest repute. From every continent, almost every country, their warning and call to action comes—'The Human Race faces mass starvation —Act Now or your children's children will die.'

Does anyone pay the slightest attention? Very few. Does anyone ever pay the slightest attention to prophets of woe? They persecute the prophets sometimes, but that is about all. The prophets were so frequently right that I have often marvelled at the persistent deafness of mankind to all warnings of preventable horrors to come. I have come to the conclusion that the explanation of this is twofold.

First, in the case of the powers that be; those in authority are always so preoccupied by the immediate problems of the moment, that they have become permanently myopic and are literally incapable of taking any but the shortest of short-term views. At the present time, for example, the need for timber, for fuel and housing *now*, is of such apparently prime importance that it seems to justify the risk that a new desert will result to-morrow. It is a mistaken view, of course, and it is the attitude of mind that has produced the dustbowls of the world and landed us in the mess we are in; a mess which makes it increasingly more difficult to opt for the long-term view. One can have nothing but sympathy with those who may have to choose between the death of hundreds now or millions to-morrow. There is always the chance that if one saves the hundreds now one will not live to see the million perish. Thus it is—to take a topical example—that the present danger from the atomic bomb appears much greater than that from soil erosion. It isn't. In point of fact it is a mere flea-bite to it when considered in terms of the probable survival of the species, but that is the way it *looks*, so those in authority perpetually confuse priorities and postpone action, while the apathy of the rest of the population comes, I think, from the feeling that nothing they personally can do about it can possibly affect the situation as a whole, 'so what's the use?'

I urge anyone who feels that way about it to read this book, and here I must make a confession. Like other people who have had practical experience of the results of compost-making and organic cultivation generally, I have for long been convinced that in the cycle of life the members of the soil population play a vital part, and that when relying on the return of all possible organic wastes to the soil as our sole method of fertilizing, we are not feeding our crops direct, but *through* the soil population. We have, in fact, a slogan—'Feed the soil population and they will feed your crop.' Among this vast population I have always recognized the priority claims of the earthworm as a creator of soil fertility without equal, a view confirmed and strengthened by the recent research work carried out at the Connecticut

INTRODUCTION

Agricultural Research Station which is reprinted in this book and of which I was already aware. I am even myself a breeder of domesticated earthworms in a small way. For all these reasons I did not expect to find anything particularly startling or new to me personally, in a book called *Harnessing the Earthworm*. I was wrong.

I did not know, for example, that in fertile soil the weight of bacteria alone amounts to 7,000 lb. per acre. I did not know that anywhere in cultivated soil, however fertile, the natural earthworm population reached two million per acre (Nile Valley). I did not know that in any part of the world, even where intensive propagation of earthworms for soil building was carried out, there were farms where as many as three million earthworms per acre have been recorded, and that populations of between one and two million are quite common. I did not know that one million earthworms weigh a ton, or that in the course of twenty-four hours each worm will pass through its body its own weight of soil. Since earthworm castings are composed largely of colloidal soluble humus, and are far richer in available plant foods than the surrounding soil, this represents a staggering annual deposit of natural plant fertilizer, quite apart from the continual addition of the dead bodies of the worms themselves as they fulfil their own life cycle.

The figures given in this book of the differences in crop yields obtained from soils of equal fertility, with and without added earthworms, are startling, but not unbelievable once the data given is studied.

While I doubt whether quite such spectacular results could ever be obtained in our climate, earthworms can and do exist in a very wide range of latitudes. Where they can exist they can be increased, and there is no better or quicker way of increasing them than by intensive propagation of egg capsules in special breeding boxes. The point being that when transferred as *eggs* to their final location in garden, field or orchard, they will survive, whereas the mature or growing worm may not.

The technique for this intensive propagation is simple, and Dr. Barrett gives such clear and concise instructions that anyone —whether he starts with purchased stock or native brandlings—

INTRODUCTION

can test the claims made for it for himself. For the English reader, however, there is one serious omission. The optimum temperature for maximum production of egg capsules is given as 70 degrees, and while plenty of advice is given for protecting culture boxes or master beds from too great heat, nothing whatever is said about how to protect them from cold. My own experience may therefore be helpful. Culture *in boxes* must either be discontinued during the winter, or take place in cellars or heated greenhouses. Culture in master beds can continue provided these are sunk in the ground and covered up with straw in frosty weather. Attention of course must be given to drainage from below, and prevention of flooding from above.

I consider it highly important that experiments on the lines suggested in this book should be carried out without delay. As organic cultivators are well aware, the principal argument used against them by soil scientists, is based on mathematics. 'The crop takes out more than the compost puts back. The result must be a deficiency.' The organic cultivator replies that the proof of the pudding is in the eating, which he can demonstrate. Therefore, either mathematics do not apply to living organisms, or there must be some figures missing from the sum. It seems to me that this book gives a clue to one at least of the possible missing figures, and I hope our scientists will give it the study it deserves. Mankind is at the last frontier. There is no new soil to be had in the horizontal plane. His hope lies in building new soil vertically. Dr. Barrett asserts that by harnessing the earthworm in the way he recommends, the kitchen waste or garbage from a household of two or three members will furnish enough ideal earthworm food to breed tens of thousands of the soil builders each year. He himself, by this method, produces all the fruit and vegetables he and his family can eat, from one acre of land, as well as growing flowers and lawns. He discovered, in an experiment in his culture beds, that an acre of soil, if provided with enough organic matter, could support an astronomical population of earthworms, and quotes the Oregon State and New York State College of Forestry field studies as indicating that an earthworm population of from 250,000 to 1,500,000 an acre is

xv

enough to keep the earth as fertile and productive as man can want it.

In another publication, Dr. Barrett sums the matter up thus: 'The problem facing civilization to-day is rebuilding the soil and restoring the earth to a form immediately usable for food production. By the slow process of nature, it takes 500 to 1,000 years to lay down an inch of topsoil. Under favourable conditions a task-force of earthworms can do the same job in five years. An individual working with a lug-box or a compost pile can start building topsoil for his garden. A farmer working with a manure pile can do it with his farm. A community utilizing a garbage dump can do it, or a nation working with its resources can do it.'

When, in connection with my work for the Soil Association, I have lectured on world soil erosion and the imperative need to restore, maintain and if possible increase the vitality of what soil is left, people often say, 'I realize the situation is appalling, but what can *I* do?' I feel this book at last contains a practical answer to that question. 'Feed earthworms.' This answer may sound flippant. I don't think you will think so when you have read this book. The technique is easy, and involves much less work than ordinary compost-making, and in all seriousness I suggest that if everyone turned his attention to increasing the earthworm population (and there is no one who cannot do this, for it can be done even in a flower-pot or window-box) it might be the key to the survival of the human race, because through utilizing all organic wastes to feed earthworms and then deliberately putting them to work in the manner here described, it might be possible not only vastly to increase the fertility and productivity of the land already under cultivation, but also to arrest the further advance of deserts and dustbowls. This would give humanity a breathing space in which to learn how to bring other creative forces into play, so that water and life and the capacity to sustain vegetation may ultimately be restored to all the man-made deserts of the earth.

EVE B. BALFOUR

PART ONE

THE EARTHWORM
AND ITS ENVIRONMENT

I

HUMUS

All flesh is one, including man, in its demand for nutrition to survive, but man alone demands infinitely more than mere nutrition. Through his conquest over the forces of nature, man has adapted himself to all conditions and environments and lives wherever there is air to breathe—on the surface of the earth, in the sky, under the earth, on the surface of the waters, under the sea. His frozen footprints are preserved for future ages in the regions of the north pole and the trail of the tractor pushes steadily into the unexplored continent locked in everlasting winter around the south pole. His air-conditioning creates a cool spot for luxurious comfort astride the Equator, and he squats nonchalantly within the rim of boiling volcanic cauldrons and takes the temperature of mother earth and diagnoses her fevers and convulsions.

To serve the demands of the ubiquitous adaptability of man, to speed up production of necessities and luxuries for his use, to create new and useful things to satisfy his growing needs and desires, are some of the practical ends of scientific research. Because of his adaptability and conquest over the forces of nature, man has cut loose from his mother's apron strings—the earth—and we find the populations of civilization throughout the world, in large part, marooned on the islands of villages, towns, and cities, segregated and separated from the land—vast aggregations of restless, discontented children, playing with the machine and toys which science and invention have provided and uniting in a mighty cry and cosmic bawl for food.

Let the flow of food to the cities stop for a single day, and its cessation is headline news. Let the flow stop for two days, and it becomes tragedy of major proportions. Let it stop for a week, and panic seizes the people as starvation takes hold.

In checking over the annual requisition of the human family

3

for food and supplies, we are staggered by such items as these:
Rush the harvest of 4,954,000,000 bushels of wheat, and prepare
366,000,000 acres of land for replanting. Husk 4,942,000,000
bushels of corn and prepare 209,100,000 acres of land for replanting. Round up 182,365,000 head of cattle for beef and but-
ter, milk and shoes. Ship 38,159,000 bales of cotton to the factories, with 3,692,000,000 pounds of wool, that we may be
clothed and kept warm. And in the United States, where they
are peculiarly peanut-conscious, we find a small item of
1,291,655,000 pounds of peanuts; also a citrus fruit item of
67,067,000 boxes.

In the annual Year-Book of the United States Department
of Agricultural Statistics, several hundred pages of fine print are
required to tabulate and report on the annual food crops of the
United States and the world. Mentioned above are a few of the
major items that are included in the annual demands of the
human family for food and clothing. The size of the order is
briefly indicated so as to call attention to the fact that the basic
source of all these materials is humus, the immediately usable
supply of which is concentrated in the eighteen-inch surface
crust of the earth and in the more favoured and very limited
areas of the globe. And humus is not found in inexhaustible
mines below the surface of the earth—in the better soils it
diminishes almost to vanishing point at a depth of thirty-six
inches. It is there potentially, just as food is potentially present
in the crude elements of the earth.

Humus is the end product of plant and animal life and must
be created for current use from day to day and season to season.
In the cycle of nature, the available material must be used over
and over again; it is nature's method to convert, transmute, dis-
integrate, rebuild. All vegetation, all life, contributes its quota.
From the single-celled yeast plant floating in the wind to the
majestic *sequoia gigantea*, towering nearly three hundred feet
into the air, from microbe to man—all have been couched in the
bedding ground of humus. And all eventually find their way to
the common burial place—the compost heap of nature—to be
converted into humus and serve in the unbroken cycle of nature.

For the most part, the populations of the earth dwell along

4

seashores and lakes, along rivers in the valleys, and in the low-lying foothills and great plains of the torrid and temperate zones, where the great humus factories of nature are located. Because water runs downhill, this is so. From the dust-laden winds of the desert, from star dust and the dust of disintegrating comets and planets, from the weathered face of the rocks and hills and mountains, nature gathers her materials, and from the mother-waters of the sea she creates the rains and washes the atmosphere. And in the end, from the millions of square miles of high ground, the waters find their way into all the settling basins of the earth to deposit the elements of life in the humus factories of nature.

THE HUMUS FACTORY

In her vast humus factories, nature uses many processes—slow combustion, chemical disintegration, bacterial decomposition, fermentation, heat, light, darkness, wind and rain, frost and sun—and earthworms; all these unite, finally, to form that thin surface layer of dark earth in which life is rooted. As volumes have been written and are constantly being written on these many processes through which nature attains her ends, I shall not burden these pages with detailed discussion on this subject. Suffice it to say that many of the processes are slow, requiring years, centuries, ages—yes, aeons of time; for the first thin blanket of parent material of humus which was spread over the surface of the earth in preparation for the birth of life was the deposit of star dust, disintegrating planets and comets, and the invisible particles brought to the earth by the rays of the sun and other whirling bodies which are scattered, like wind-blown particles of dust, throughout the infinite reaches of space.

Taking the earth as we find it, the creation of humus from dead vegetation and animal life is usually a process measured in terms of weeks and months, or a number of years, with one notable exception: When a requisition is put in for a few million tons of humus, to be prepared overnight for emergency plant food for to-morrow, nature marshals her vast earthworm army to a feast; and, behold, the miracle is accomplished—the order is filled and the crying children of the plant world are fed—the night-soil of earthworms, castings, is deposited on and near the surface of the earth, ready for immediate use—for *earthworms excrete humus.* No waiting, no worry, no confusion—just the ordinary, routine, daily transaction of business in the humus factories of nature.

Earthworms are the shock-troops of nature for the quick production of humus while she is waiting upon her slower processes. Climaxing her millions of years of experimentation, she created in miniature a perfect humus mill, easily adapted to the use of man. In the body of the earthworm we find a complete, high-speed humus factory, combining all the processes—both mechanical and chemical—for turning out the finished product, topsoil, properly conditioned for best root growth and containing in rich proportion and in water-soluble form all the elements required of the earth for plant nutrition.

THE EARTHWORM FAMILY

For detailed information and classification of earthworms in general, I refer the reader to the voluminous writings on the subject of earthworms which may be found in the Zoology section in the reference department of most public libraries. We are here interested in the function and work of earthworms rather than in a study of the animal from a zoological standpoint.

While many hundreds of species, including marine worms, are comprised in the order *Phylum annelida,* our interest centres in the *Oligochaeta* and that portion known to science as the 'small-bristled ringed worm'. They are distributed all over the planet, including the islands of the sea, from the tropics to extreme northern and southern latitudes, except in the Arctic and sub-Arctic regions and glacial and sub-glacial regions where the ground may be frozen to great depths over long periods of time.

In size, earthworms range all the way from small worms of almost microscopic dimensions to giant annelids measuring from three feet to eleven feet long. The larger members of the family are found in certain parts of South America, Africa, Ceylon and Australia. The largest of the giant worms, *Megascolides Austra-*

6

lis, is found in Australia, where authentic measurements of worms up to eleven feet in length have been made.

In the torrid and temperate zones more than one thousand species of earthworm (some authorities say more than eighteen hundred) live and procreate. Whatever the name, size, or habitat, earthworms have one important characteristic in common —they swallow the earth with all that it contains, and in the process of digestion and elimination excrete practically neutral humus—topsoil rich in water-soluble nutrients for plant life.

Narrowing the field down still more to the particular purpose of this inquiry, I am interested in the group of earthworms common to the United States and known under various popular and colloquial names, such as 'angleworms', 'dewworms', 'night crawlers', 'night lions', 'fishworms', 'rainworms', etc. The last name, 'Regenwurm', is very generally used in the extensive German literature on the subject.

For practical purposes and for reasons given later, I shall eliminate from consideration all worms except the rainworm (*Lumbricus terrestris*), illustrated in Plate I(a), and the brandling, or stinking earthworm (*Helodrilus foetidus*), also illustrated in Plate I. The brandling is commonly known as the manure worm.

The rainworm is a native of the fields and forest, lawns, gardens, orchards, meadows, and pastures. It commonly lives in the upper eighteen inches of soil, devouring ceaselessly, day and night, dead roots, leaves, and all dead organic materials, digesting and utilizing them to serve its bodily needs and finally ejecting humus in the form of castings—the manure of earthworms. But the rainworm is not entirely concerned with the thin surface layer of the earth, though that surface layer is its main feeding and breeding ground. It quite generally burrows to a depth of five or six feet, and earthworm burrows have even been found at depths of from ten to fourteen feet. From these deep burrows into the subsoil the earthworm returns to the surface, bringing new mineral parent material for topsoil and depositing it in the form of castings. These castings from the deep layers of the earth surface are not just sterile, mineralized earth. In the journey through the alimentary canal of the worm they have undergone chemical changes, taken on new material, been ground and thoroughly mixed, and when they are deposited on and in the immediate surface of the earth this new material has become humus-laden topsoil, ready for immediate use by growing vegetation.

In the colder climates, the rainworm burrows deep below the frost line during the winter season, lying dormant while the ground is frozen, but coming to the surface as soon as the spring thaw has warmed the earth. However, the rainworm is very hardy, remains active in quite low temperatures, and has even been observed in slushy snow.

Under particularly favourable conditions, the rainworm often attains a length of twelve inches or more. A more usual length for a fully mature rainworm is five or six inches, with an average length of eight inches.

The brandling, or manure worm (*Helodrilus foetidus*), is a small, very active, very prolific worm, characterized by a disagreeable odour when crushed or injured. Its favourite habitat is manure piles and compost heaps, hence its name 'manure worm'. Contrary to general belief, however, the manure worm readily adapts itself to the same environments favoured by the rainworm. The brandling gorges voraciously on manure and decaying vegetation, digesting, deodorizing and converting all such material into rich, clean humus, with an odour similar to fresh-turned meadow earth. The castings of the manure worm, like those of the rainworm and the many other species of earthworm, contain a very high percentage of water-soluble plant nutrients.

The manure worm is not a deep-burrowing worm like its relative the rainworm, but prefers to work in the surface areas under rotting vegetation, manure, and other decaying materials. However, after becoming adapted to the soil, it is soon a good burrower and will take care of itself in almost all climates. The manure worm is found widely distributed throughout the United States and in Europe, in the southern as well as in the colder latitudes. In size, it may attain a length of six inches or more, but in measuring a large number of mature manure worms we determined an average length of about four inches. In intensive propagation and use of earthworms, size is important and the smaller varieties can be utilized with better results than can the larger worms. This point will be emphasized later.

Finally, when I come to the subject of the intensive propagation and use of earthworms in soil-building for agriculture, horticulture, orcharding, nursery, and home gardening, I shall discuss somewhat at length what I have termed 'domesticated earthworms'. The term 'domesticated' is applied to earthworms which have been developed through selective breeding and feeding methods in a controlled environment especially created to favour intensive propagation, as opposed to native earthworms which are found in most fertile, well-watered soils.

From this brief discussion of the earthworm family, I pass to a consideration of the feeding habits and digestive functions of earthworms, which make them possibly the most valuable animals on earth.

INTESTINES OF THE EARTH

We are indebted to the ancient Greek philosopher, Aristotle, for the apt phrase which literally describes the function of these master-builders of topsoil. He called earthworms 'intestines of the earth'. W. L. Powers, Soil Scientist, Oregon Agricultural Experiment Station, termed the earthworm a 'colloid mill'. This, too, is a very good descriptive name to indicate the activity of earthworms in soil-building. They literally serve as colloid mills to produce the intimate chemical and mechanical homogenized mixture of fine organic and inorganic matter which forms their castings. In the mixing which takes place in the alimentary canal of the earthworm, the ingested materials undergo chemical changes, deodorization and neutralization, so that the resultant castings (manure) are a practically neutral humus, rich in water-soluble plant food, immediately available for plant nutrition.

As flexible as silk, as strong as steel—these similes may well describe the body of an earthworm. Known as one of the strongest animals in nature for its size, an earthworm weighing less than one-thirtieth of an ounce may move a stone weighing as much as two ounces. The family name, *annelida*, derived from the Latin word *anellus* (a ring) is graphically descriptive

9

of the earthworm, whose body is formed by a series of from two hundred to four hundred muscular rings (more or less, depending on the species), closely woven together to form a tube of great strength, stream-lined to the ultimate for functional performance.

Considered primarily, man himself is an organism of bone and muscle, brain and nervous system, organ and tissue, integrated around a digestive tube—the alimentary canal—about thirty feet long. The earthworm is a digestive tube alone, stripped of all external encumbrance which might interfere with its life-function of digestion, and equipped with just enough instinctive intelligence to carry out its feeding activities without too fine discrimination.

Thus, everything which opposes itself to the blind attention of the earthworm becomes something to be devoured. When a stone too large to swallow is encountered, the worm eats its way around, giving the surface a chemical treatment in passing and possibly sucking off a few choice morsels from the weathered surface. If small enough, the particle is swallowed, to serve as a millstone in the gizzard while being subjected to the solvent action of acids and alkalis so abundantly provided in the digestive secretions. If a piece of tough cellulose, such as dry leaf stem, twig, or bit of wood, is met with, it may be coated with a saliva-like secretion and left to soften (perhaps for days or weeks), later to resume its journey of disintegration and digestion through the tubular intestinal mill. Figuratively speaking, the worm says 'the world is my oyster', and then proceeds literally to swallow it with everything it may contain.

To be more specific, in action the earthworm employs the principle of the hydraulic drill, softening the earth in front of it, if necessary, with its secretions and sucking it into its mouth. Thus, blindly, the worm eats its dark way through the densest earth, including tough, compact adobe and clay soils, riddling and honeycombing the soil to a depth of ten feet or more with aerating tunnels or burrows, as it swallows the earth with all that it contains—dead roots, vegetable and animal remains, bacteria, the minute and microscopic vegetable life of the soil, and mineral elements. Being truly a blind dweller of the dark,

10

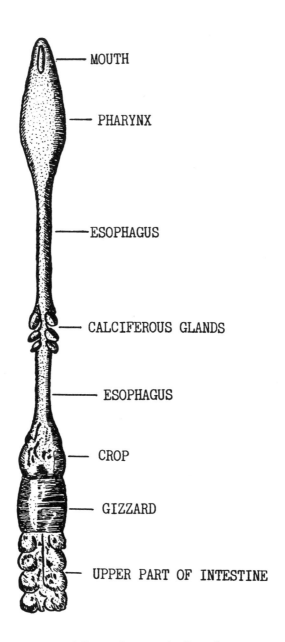

FIG. 1. Alimentary canal of earthworm
(*After Charles Darwin*)

highly sensitive to light, the earthworm is a nocturnal animal, coming to the surface at night to feed on organic litter. By day it pushes slow tunnelling operations below the surface, the softened and almost liquefied material finding its way into the storage space of the worm's crop.

Paul Griswold Howes, Curator of Natural History at the Bruce Museum of Natural History, U.S.A., gives this concise statement of the feeding habits of worms in his wonderfully interesting book, *Backyard Exploration*:

'Worms are the most numerous at the surface of the ground at night. . . . They come to the surface to feed, as they are truly nocturnal animals. . . . They do actually consume large quantities of vegetable matter—not living leaves and grass, but the dead and dying vegetable matter that lies upon the ground. Holding fast in their burrows by the tail-end, the worms reach out in all directions, stretching themselves to great lengths and grasping bits of food, which they pull below the surface. Here part of the material is eaten, while vast quantities of it pass into vegetable mould that helps to make other plants grow. (Editorial note: All vegetable remains not immediately consumed, are eventually eaten and pass through the alimentary canals of worms in their final transformation into humus or soluble plant food.)

'In addition to the vegetable matter which worms eat, great quantities of soil also pass through this vast army. From this soil they assimilate what is useful to them, leaving the remainder each night upon the surface in the lobed and familiar castings which everyone has seen. Stop for a minute to consider the countless individual worms which inhabit every acre of ground. Think then of the weight and depth of a single year's castings that are left upon the surface and you will begin to realize that the worms are actually responsible for the ploughing and turning over of the earth as the years go by.'

Continuing our journey through the earthworm, all the ingested material—vegetable matter, animal matter, living and dead bacteria, mineral earth, small stones, etc.—passes into the crop and thence into the gizzard as a semi-liquid, plastic mass, carrying its own grindstones. In the gizzard everything is subjected to the grinding, disintegrating and mixing action of this efficient organ, as the abundant digestive juices are poured in to exert their chemical and solvent action. No form of organic material escapes, for the digestive secretions of the earthworm are similar to those of the higher animals, including the human family. Carbohydrates, fats, proteins, cellulose—all are grist for the mill of the earthworm; for anything that cannot be digested is at least so finely comminuted that no structural form remains.

Special mention should be made of the highly remarkable calciferous glands which are located in the walls of the oesophagus of the earthworm. Nothing like them is known in any other animal. These calcium-secreting glands pour out abundant quantities of fluid rich in calcium, which exerts its neutralizing action upon the acids of the organic and inorganic mass of material which daily passes through the alimentary canal of the earthworm—a quantity which may equal or exceed its own weight every twenty-four hours.

The anterior one-third of the worm's body contains the vital organs and organs of the digestive system, including the calciferous glands, crop, gizzard, and reproductive organs. The remaining two-thirds contains the intestines. As stated before, the entire worm is comprised in a muscular tube of from two hundred to four hundred strongly contractile muscular rings, the number of rings varying in different species.

Continuing with the digestive process, after being discharged from the gizzard into the intestine, the material is subjected to further mixing action as it is moved slowly along the alimentary canal, taking on valuable added elements from the intestinal and urinary secretions in which it is continually bathed. Particularly valuable is the admixture of the urinary secretions, on account of the ammonia content. In *Principles and Practice of Agricultural Analysis*, Dr. Harvey W. Wiley states:

'A considerable portion of the ammonia in the soil at any given time may also be due to the action of worms, as much as ·018 per cent of this substance having been found in their excrement (castings). It is probable that nearly the whole of the vegetable matter in the soil passes sooner or later through the alimentary canal of these ceaseless soil-builders, and is converted into the form of humus.'

In its passage through the worm, such nutriment as may be necessary for the worm's own body-building and functioning is absorbed from the humidified, semi-liquid, and emulsified material. After having performed this nutritional function, the material is finally ejected as castings—such finely divided, thoroughly homogenized earth that only chemical analysis can resolve it into its component parts. In other words, the ultimate end-product of the activity of earthworms is humus—the clean, sweet-smelling substance of new-turned earth—the bedding, rooting, and growing material of life itself.

WHY AND HOW

In considering the soil-building possibilities inherent in harnessing the earthworm, the subject matter naturally falls under two main headings, viz.: 'Why It Can Be Done' and 'How It Can Be Done'. The preceding sections have been introductory to these two divisions. As a preliminary generality, we might say, 'The reason it can be done is because it has been done'. The remaining chapters of this book are really an elaboration of this generality.

At this point I feel justified in a brief digression to consider the practical purposes of soil-building, as I conceive it.

Collectively, we think of man as the master of the earth, through his universal adaptability, harnessing, controlling, and directing the forces of nature. Through his adaptability, the present-day environment of man has become the entire earth. Thanks to his ability to comprehend, direct and utilize the forces of nature, he can now live in comparative comfort wherever there is air to breathe. Nevertheless, to-day and in all the days to come, each individual is encompassed by his own particular environment and must work out his own salvation in that environment.

Philosophically, we listen to the full-bellied poet blithely singing, 'I am the master of my fate, the captain of my soul'. But until the individual can paraphrase the poet with a more literal and

14

practical statement, 'I am the master of the earth, the captain of the soil', he is liable to live in insecurity and fear of the future. Security—what a comforting word! Security means adequate food—a roof over one's head—clothes on one's back—a place in the sun—freedom from fear—no apprehension for the future. To the individual who desires surely to build security for himself and his loved ones, we hope to bring a knowledge of the means through which he may become the literal master of his own earth.

All the necessities, comforts, satisfactions, and luxuries of civilization wait upon the production of food—and food comes from topsoil. As a master-builder of topsoil throughout the ages, the earthworm in nature has played a leading role. Under scientific control and intensive propagation, the earthworm is destined to play a major part in the future development of topsoil and its maintenance at the highest point of productive capacity.

The topsoil of the future, beginning with the immediate present, will be built by man exactly to meet his balanced food requirements. Working intelligently with the same tools, materials, and forces with which nature has worked throughout the ages, but in highly accelerated tempo, each individual, here and now, may begin to build his own soil. Whether the individual works with a single flower-pot or window-box, a few square feet of earth in a city yard, or in a roomy garden, on orchard or farm, each man, woman, and child can put the earthworm to work, with all the allied forces of nature and cheaply abundant materials at hand, and begin to build security for all the to-morrows of the future.

THE NEW FRONTIER

The crowding populations of the earth stand on the last frontier—a new frontier. Circling the globe, they have met. There are no more horizons, marking the boundary of a new and better Promised Land. Among conflicting ideologies and changing social systems, a basic fact stands out: We cannot move east or west, north or south—here we stand and must stand.

At this point, the reader may appropriately ask a few questions: What is this new frontier, upon which I am apparently standing? Where is it? I am anxious to explore it, adapt myself and build security for me and mine. And, incidentally, where do earthworms come into the picture?

The new frontier is literally beneath our feet. Layer by layer, right down to the bedrock, the ancient remains of buried continents lie sleeping—the inexhaustible parent material of new and fertile virgin lands to be awakened and roused to verdant life through the knowledge and mastery of man. This new frontier is not a figure of speech; it is an actual, physical fact—and each individual can go to work at once upon his own particular spot of ground, be it small or large, and have the pleasure, satisfaction, and profit of enjoying his own new earth which he himself has helped to create.

When the struggle for the mastery of the earth—the actual physical occupation of the earth—is over, vast changes will take place, are already taking place. Among the changes very definitely in evidence is the movement of city and urban populations toward the land. Spurred by necessity and a universal awakening to the importance of the soil, millions of people are turning toward the establishment of themselves upon the land, either small plots or more extensive acreage, according to their ability to acquire. They are seeking security through the development of a subsistence-homestead as a vocation or avocation.

The wise man or woman will not procrastinate, but will begin to plan now to occupy a little piece of earth, or a big piece of earth, and learn how to utilize it to the best advantage. It is not necessary to seek expensive land, highly developed and fertile. Through simple and easily mastered methods of soil-building, utilizing earthworms and allied forces of nature, the land-dweller can build his own good soil in any quantity necessary to meet his needs.

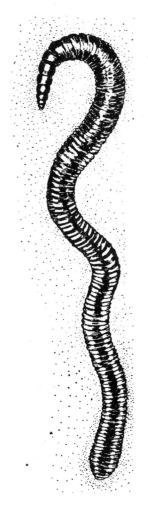

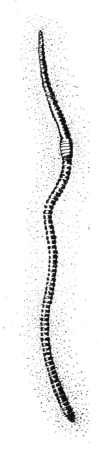

PLATE I. (b)

The Brandling, or Stinking Earthworm, *Helodrilus foetidus*, natural size (Hofmeister)

PLATE I. (a)

The Rainworm, *Lumbricus terrestris*, natural size. (Hofmeister)

PLATE II. Dr. George Sheffield Oliver, with a cluster of ripe 'carob' against the background

II

THE EARTHWORM IN NATURE

In the primordial gases of chaos nature initiated her soil-building activities to be continued uninterrupted down through the ages. The primary parent material of soil is stone. 'Soil', wrote Shaler, 'is rock material on its way toward the deep.' In the age-long weathering and disintegration of stone, nature uses her many forces—mechanical, chemical, and vital. Down from the heights, the comminuted particles find their way, to be deposited and mixed for a spell with a vast aggregate of vegetable and animal residues in the low-lying places of the earth, but in the end to find their way on flood-borne waters to the sea.

The incalculable animal and vegetable life of the sea finds its end in death, to settle into the depths with all the debris from earth, eventually to be compressed into sedimentary rock. Through erosion, mountains are ground down, entire continents levelled. Through great seismic upheavals and the deposition of silt, continents once again rise from the waters, to tower into mountains, hills and plains; again to be slowly worn to powder and redeposited in the sea.

Thus, in a never-ending cycle, the surface of the earth changes —breaking up, becoming soil, becoming vegetable and animal, becoming soil again, over and over again; and finally ending in the deeps, to be compressed into sedimentary rock and once again, through geological ages, to rise above the surface and complete the recurring cycle.

Working through remote geological ages down to the present in practically unchanged form, the earthworm has been and is one of the great integrating, soil-building forces of nature. In this movement of 'rock material on its way to the deep', all life, both vegetable and animal, has contributed to make the subsoil and topsoil the great repository of the physical elements of life— oxygen, nitrogen, calcium, phosphorus, potassium, sodium, mag-

C   17

nesium, sulphur, silicon, hydrogen, chlorine, iron, with traces of practically all the known elements of the universe. In the building of this repository, the earthworm has contributed a major part, for practically all of the fertile topsoil of earth's surface has passed many times through the bodies of earthworms. In the book *Man and the Earth*, the noted Harvard geologist, Nathaniel Southgate Shaler, has aptly called the thin layer of humus-bearing topsoil 'the placenta of life'. Continuing, Shaler warns: 'Man and all forms of life draw life from the sun, clouds, air, and earth through a tenuous film of topsoil, indispensable and, if rudely handled, impermanent.' In the continual renewal and maintenance of this important surface layer upon which life depends, the earthworm is one of the greatest tools of nature.

Animal life in all its forms, from microbe to man, is the great transformer of vegetation into perfect earthworm food, the animal life itself, in the end, becoming food for the earthworm. In the process of transformation a small percentage becomes animal tissue, but most of it becomes food for humus-building worms. In the feeding of one hundred pounds of grain to domestic animals, such as cattle, sheep and pigs, on the average 89½ pounds becomes excrement, waste and gases, with only 10½ pounds accounted for by increase in animal weight. Aside from the gaseous waste, the 89½ pounds represents earthworm food. In a never-ending annual cycle untold millions of tons of the products of forest and farm, orchard and garden, rivers, lakes, and oceans, are harvested, to be transformed into earthworm food after they have nourished animal life and served man. All the biological end-products of life—kitchen and farm waste, stubble, dead vegetation, manures, dead animal residues—constitute the cheap and ever-renewed source of earthworm food for profitable soil-building.

The microscopic life of the earth and soil is vastly greater than the animal life which we see on and above the earth as beasts, birds and man. In fertile farm land, where it has been handled by organic methods, we may find as high as seven thousand pounds of bacteria per acre in the superficial layer of topsoil, eternally gorging on the dead and living vegetable material, on each other and on dead animal residues—all producing earthworm food, all in turn becoming earthworm food. The unseen vegetable life of the soil—algae, fungi, moulds—form an additional great tonnage of material which eventually becomes earthworm food. The living network of fine roots, so important in holding the soil in place, constitutes about one-tenth by weight of the total organic matter in the upper six inches of soil—it is all destined to become earthworm food. In the good black soils, the organic matter—earthworm food—is represented by from one hundred and forty to as high as six hundred tons of humus per acre. The earthworm will not go hungry.

In the accumulation of the great tonnage of humus as found in the good black soils, nature has taken her time. In the slow processes of nature, it is estimated that from five hundred to one thousand years are required to lay down one inch of topsoil—seldom so short a time as five hundred years. The source of humus, as has been pointed out, is mainly vegetation. Into the structure of the plant, in the exact proportions necessary to reproduce vegetation, nature has combined the elements of nutrition for all life. These elements are derived both from the earth and from the air. Taking one thousand pounds of dry vegetation as a unit of measurement, on the average, we find upon analysis that it contains fifty pounds of chemicals derived from the earth and nine hundred and fifty pounds of chemicals derived from the air.

In the process of transition back to the soil, vegetation becomes humus. By impregnating, compounding, and combining humus with the parent mineral soil, nature slowly builds topsoil. Just as we have, from a practical standpoint, inexhaustible resources of parent mineral soil, we also have practically inexhaustible sources of vegetable material to draw upon for purposes of soil-building, sources which have never heretofore been exploited for the use of man.

19

III

THE EARTHWORM IN SCIENTIFIC LITERATURE

So thoroughly established and accepted is the place and function of the earthworm in nature that soil scientists, and other scientific writers in general, give it brief mention in a paragraph, or possibly one or two pages, as the most important animal agency in soil-building, and then refer the reader to Charles Darwin's classic study as recorded in his great book, *The Formation of Vegetable Mould Through the Action of Earthworms, with Observations on Their Habits.*

Beginning his study of the earthworm during his college days prior to 1837, Charles Darwin collected his notes, made his observations, and set them down in meticulous and painstaking detail throughout his long life. In 1881, shortly before the death of the great naturalist, the first edition of his famous book on earthworms appeared. Thus in this one instance we have a complete and comprehensive study over a sufficient period of time in which to establish facts and form conclusions. To appreciate and comprehend fully the vast activity and importance of earthworms in nature, Darwin's book on *The Formation of Vegetable Mould* should be read. It is available in practically all public libraries.

'Vegetable mould' is the name given by Darwin to the fertile layers of topsoil. In his introduction, referring to his studies and observations, he states: 'I was thus led to conclude that all the vegetable mould over the whole country has passed many times through, and will again pass many times through, the intestinal canals of worms. Hence the term "animal mould" would be in some respects more appropriate than that commonly used, "vegetable mould".' In a summing-up of Darwin's conclusions, we cannot do better than to quote from his own summary, given in the last chapter of his book. We quote in part:

20

EARTHWORM IN SCIENTIFIC LITERATURE

'Worms have played a more important part in the history of the world than most persons would at first suppose. In almost all humid countries they are extraordinarily numerous, and for their size possess great muscular power. In many parts of England a weight of more than ten tons (10,516 kilograms) of dry earth annually passes through their bodies and is brought to the surface on each acre of land; so that the whole superficial bed of vegetable mould passes through their bodies in the course of every few years. From the collapsing of the old burrows the mould is in constant though slow movement, and the particles composing it are thus rubbed together. By these means fresh surfaces are continually exposed to the action of the carbonic acid in the soil, and of the humus-acids which appear to be still more efficient in the decomposition of rocks. The generation of the humus-acids is probably hastened during the digestion of the many half-decayed leaves which worms consume. Thus, the particles of earth forming the superficial mould are subjected to conditions eminently favourable to their decomposition and disintegration. Moreover, the particles of the softer rocks suffer some amount of mechanical trituration in the muscular gizzards of the worms, in which small stones serve as mill-stones. . . .

'Worms prepare the ground in an excellent manner for the growth of fibrous-rooted plants and for seedlings of all kinds. They periodically expose the mould to the air, and sift it so that no stones larger than the particles which they can swallow are left in it. They mingle the whole intimately together, like a gardener who prepares fine soil for his choicest plants. In this state it is well fitted to retain moisture and to absorb all soluble substances, as well as for the process of nitrification. The bones of dead animals, the harder part of insects, the shell of land molluscs, leaves, twigs, etc., are before long all buried beneath the accumulated castings of worms, and are thus brought in a more or less decayed state within reach of the roots of plants. Worms likewise drag an infinite number of dead leaves, and other parts of plants into their burrows, partly for the sake of plugging them up and partly as food.

'The leaves which are dragged into the burrows as food, after being torn into the finest shreds, partially digested and

21

saturated with the intestinal and urinary secretions, are commingled with much earth. This earth forms the dark-coloured, rich humus which almost everywhere covers the surface of the land with a fairly well-defined layer or mantle. . . .

'When we behold a wide, turf-covered expanse, we should remember that its smoothness, on which so much of its beauty depends, is mainly due to all the inequalities having been slowly levelled by worms. It is a marvellous reflection that the whole of the superficial mould over any such expanse has passed, and will again pass, every few years through the bodies of worms. The plough is one of the most ancient and most valuable of man's inventions; but long before he existed the land was in fact regularly ploughed, and still continues to be ploughed, by earthworms. It may be doubted whether there are many other animals which have played so important a part in the history of the world as have these lowly organized creatures.'

In some of the soils of England, Darwin found earthworms in concentrations of from 25,000 to 53,000 per acre, passing through their bodies and bringing to the surface from ten to eighteen tons of dry earth annually on each acre of land. Later investigations, carried out by the British Government in a more favourable location than England, showed an annual volume of castings averaging more than two hundred tons per acre. Notable investigators from the time of Darwin down to the immediate present have corroborated his findings and have also shown that Darwin was extremely conservative in his claims, both as to numbers of earthworms per acre and tonnage of castings thrown up.

Dr. Firman E. Bear, formerly professor of Soils, Ohio State University, in his authoritative book on *Theory and Practice in the Use of Fertilizers*, states: 'In a study of earthworms in the soil on the Ohio State University Farm, it was found that they were present in plots of soil covered with bluegrass in numbers averaging over one million per acre. These were concentrated, at the time the numbers were estimated in July, in the upper foot of soil.'

In a radio address delivered over WGY Farm Forum, Prof. Svend O. Heiberg, of the New York State College of Forestry, said: 'If your soil is suitable for earthworms . . . there may be more than two and one-half million per acre, weighing about fourteen hundred pounds. That means that you may have more pounds of earthworms in your employment than all your domestic animals put together.'

Mr. Arthur J. Mason, testifying as an expert before the Committee on Flood Control, House of Representatives, Seventieth Congress, stated: 'The weight of the angleworms in this country is at least tenfold the weight of the entire human population.' Mr. Mason estimated that the farm lands of Illinois, his home state, in normal circumstances, contain an earthworm population of more than six hundred billion.

Hundreds of quotations from scientific literature could be cited, corroborative of the foregoing, but it is unnecessary to burden these pages with further examples.

SOIL-BUILDERS OF FOREST LANDS

Curtis Fletcher Marbut, noted soil scientist and for many years Chief of the Soil Survey Division in the United States Department of Agriculture, expressed the belief that in certain areas the granular condition characterizing whole layers of soil is due to earthworm casts. We quote from 'Soils and Men', U.S. Department of Agriculture Year-book for 1938, page 946:

'Certain mulls, or granular mixtures of mineral and organic material produced by earthworms, give particular areas of the forest floor their whole character.'

Quoting further from the same book in the chapter on 'Formation of Soil', pages 964–5, we find:

'Earthworms feed on soil and organic matter and thoroughly mix soils in which they live. They move and enrich many tons of soil to the acre each year, and they thrive especially well in moderately acid to moderately alkaline soils. One of the many indications of potentially productive soils is the presence of well-nourished earthworms.'

From the *Journal of Forestry*, Vol. 37, No. 1, we quote the following from an article on 'Forest Soil in Relation to Silviculture', by Svend O. Heiberg, Associate Professor of Siviculture, New York State College of Forestry. The quotation refers to one main type of forest soil, 'mull', or 'crumbmull':

    'In the mull, the organic matter is intimately mixed with the upper few inches of the mineral soil. In its best form it is crumbly, friable and porous. It resembles a well-cultivated garden. The mixing is done by the soil fauna, especially by the earthworms which continually dig and cultivate and eat both the vegetable matter and the mineral soil. The excreta are placed upon the soil surface; in fact, the entire humus layer of coarse mull consists of earthworm excreta. In good forest mull between one and two million earthworms are found per acre, weighing about eight hundred pounds; their castings may amount to fifteen tons per acre per year. There is no doubt that earthworms are the most beneficial animals in forestry. The cultivation of the soil and ploughing under of manure which farmers and gardeners find to be of great importance for the soil productivity is done "free" by the earthworms if they are furnished with a suitable environment. . . . With respect to productivity, this humus type (coarse mull) is undoubtedly the highest and its ability to absorb moisture and thus prevent surface run-off and erosion is high. One litre of water poured on a 100 square centimetres surface of coarse mull—which corresponds to about four inches of rain—may be absorbed in less than fifteen seconds, while on the same soil where the coarse mull has not developed it may require two or three hours to seep in.'

MASS-PRODUCTION OF TOPSOIL ON FARM LAND

    To show just what the earthworm can accomplish in soil-building when given a proper chance, we must select a spot in the world where nature has provided a favourable environment, with an unfailing supply of earthworm food in excessive abundance, properly composted with all the chemical elements and organic content required to build rich topsoil. Fortunately, we have such an example in the Valley of the Nile, ancient 'breadbasket' of the world and reputedly the most fertile soil on the face of the globe. Only in the more densely populated areas of China and Japan do we find such concentration of human beings drawing their nourishment from limited areas of soil. For more than six thousand years of recorded history, the Valley of the Nile has been densely occupied and under continuous cultivation, and this without deterioration of the fertility of the soil. Here we have an object-lesson in nature on mass-production of topsoil on a scale of such magnitude as to enable us to envision the limitless possibilities inherent in the intensive propagation and utilization of earthworms in the controlled service of man. I shall make a brief descriptive excursion to the Upper Valley of the Nile.

THE EARTHWORMS OF THE NILE

In *United States Department of Agriculture Experiment Station Record*, Vol. 27, No. 6, we find the following summary :
'Investigations carried on by the British Government in the Valley of the White Nile in the Sudan indicate that the great fertility of the soil of this valley is due in large part to the work of earthworms. Observations are recorded from which it is estimated that the castings of earthworms on these soils during the six months of active growing season of the year amount to 239,580 pounds (119·79 tons) per acre.'

The figures given in the foregoing quotation are almost unbelievably amazing to anyone who has made no study of the activity and volume of work accomplished by earthworms. To understand them, we must examine the source of the Blue Nile and the facts in nature which make such results credible.

The two source rivers of the true Nile—White Nile and the Blue Nile—form their confluence at Khartoum, which incidentally is the mathematical midway point of this four-thousand-mile, longest river in the world. Above Khartoum between the two converging rivers, lies a triangular stretch of level country called the 'Gezira'. Roughly the Gezira is 250 miles long, 100 miles wide at the base of the triangle and narrowing to the point where the rivers unite to form the Nile. This inexhaustibly fertile, five-million-acre tract of ancient farm land has been slowly built up through the ages by the annual deposit of silt from the overflow of the Blue Nile, its waters so richly laden during the flood season that it is almost a river of mud. The land of the Gezira harbours an earthworm population, probably numbered in the billions, which is responsible for the unexcelled fertility of the soil.

We must consider the region from which the Blue Nile gathers its flood waters, in order to understand the composition of its silt. At an altitude of nine thousand feet, in the rugged highlands of Abyssinia, the Blue Nile finds its source. For nine months of the year this is a hard, dry country of volcanic mountains, abrupt, fantastic peaks, high plateaux six to ten thousand feet in elevation—vast, eroded slopes, deep gullies, narrow canyons. The river dries up to occasional water holes. To the north of the river are great timbered jungles which support an unequalled animal life, including the elephant and other herbivora, as well as the great carnivora and lesser animals of all kinds.

In June of each year comes the rainy season, beginning with torrential downpour, cloudbursts, terrific thunder and electric storms. The trickling, almost dry river wakes from its nine months' rest. Every gully, canyon, tiny tributary, and dry wash becomes a roaring torrent, as the waters from the thousands of square miles of highlands rush down to swell the Blue Nile into a vast wall of water fifteen hundred feet wide, as it starts on its course to join the White Nile at Khartoum. In its first fifty miles the river drops four thousand two hundred feet through a huge gorge, and thirty miles below Lake Tana it encounters the great fall called 'Tisitat'—'roaring fire'.

Below the falls the river is crowded into an almost inaccessible gorge, at places five thousand feet deep, between whose precipitous walls it pursues its course for five hundred miles. This gorge is an almost uninvaded jungle paradise for animals and birds. The temperature never falls below 100 degrees. The accumulated droppings of months from millions of animals and birds, including elephants, hippopotami, crocodiles, lions, leopards, and an aggregation of beasts great and small, find their way into the river to add to its rich silt. The downpour of rain continues for nearly one hundred days, with very little let-up The rushing, eroding waters from the highlands gather vast quantities of volcanic ash, ferruginous minerals, feldspar, hornblende crystals, clay, etc., down the steep hillsides into the Blue Nile, until the river carries 17 per cent of silt, of which 9 per cent is organic matter and 8 per cent mineral matter.

A peculiar element which adds appreciably to the organic richness of the silt of the Blue Nile is billions of white ants, with the numberless tons of fine earth they have piled up in their ceaseless workings during the nine months' dry season.

After flowing five hundred miles through the confines of this great canyon, a boiling, mixing cauldron of racing, silt-laden waters, the river bursts from the gorge into the lowland of the Gezira and spreads over the plain as overflow. In the Gezira more than nine thousand miles of irrigation ditches help to distribute the flood waters uniformly over the earth.

It is thus that the vast annual feast of organic and inorganic material, perfectly mixed and composted, is spread for the worms of the Gezira. Beneath the dry surface of the earth the innumerable earthworm population has awaited the coming of the rains. The earth has been riddled with billions of tunnels to a depth of several feet, making it one vast honeycombed subsurface, ready to receive and store the waters when they come. As the flood-water spreads, the thirsty earth absorbs it quickly like a sponge, leaving its deposit of silt. The earthworms begin their work and almost overnight the silt is carried through the worms, digested, homogenized and excreted as rich, fine, humus-laden topsoil, loaded with immediately available, water-soluble plant nutrients. Here no human cultivation is required. The ground is seeded and the next operation is the harvest—the earthworms do the cultivating.

Age after age, for thousands of years, this process has been repeated. In this favourable environment nature composts food in abundance, the earthworms devour it, digest it, and excrete humus for the growth of vegetation in an endless cycle. We are thus given an outstanding example of mass-production of top-soil in nature by the earthworms of the Nile Valley, rightly termed a soil of inexhaustible fertility.

In this recorded observation, the castings were estimated for a period of six months only, totalling for this time slightly less than one hundred and twenty tons per acre. Based on comprehensive knowledge of the earthworm and his work, a conservative estimate for the entire year in the area under consideration would place the total probable annual output of castings at more than two hundred tons per acre.

FERTILITY OF EARTHWORM SOIL

While engaged in research and experiments over a number of years, I examined many reports carried in scientific literature, covering a period of nearly one hundred years, from before the time of Darwin down to the immediate present. The evidence, showing vastly increased productivity of soil that is well populated with earthworms, or entirely produced by earthworms, is fully conclusive. In fact, the evidence shows an overwhelming superiority of earthworm soil over other fertile soils. Among the many reasons that account for the fertility of earthworm castings, probably the most outstanding is the fact that in its passage through the earthworm the soil undergoes a chemical change through which the nutritional elements for plant growth are rendered water-soluble to a much more highly marked degree than is found in soil which has not been subjected to the influence of earthworms.

The well-known fertility of the Nile Valley is an example—a two-thousand-mile stretch of land which is literally one vast bed of earthworm soil, ideally composted and laid down, layer by layer, and subjected to the digestion of earthworms in a favourable environment. While we have given the Valley of the Nile as an example, all the fertile river valleys and bottom lands of the earth could be cited with equal truth as illustrations of the important work of earthworms in the building of topsoil. Many plant growth experiments have been carried out in verification of the claims made for earthworm castings and soil that has been worked over by earthworms. Further on in this book we shall give other reports, but it is appropriate at this point in the discussion to cite a few.

In the book *Soils: Their Formation, Properties, Composition and Relations to Climate and Plant Growth*, by E. W. Hilgard

EARTHWORM IN SCIENTIFIC LITERATURE

(Ph.D., LL.D., one time Professor of Agriculture in the University of California and formerly Director of the California Experiment Station) we find in part[1]:

'Wolney has shown by direct experimental cultures in boxes, with and without earthworms, surprising differences between the cultural results obtained, and this has been fully confirmed by the subsequent researches of Djemil. In Wolney's experiments, the ratio of higher production in the presence of worms varied all the way from 2·6 per cent in the case of oats, 63·9 per cent in that of rye, 135·9 per cent in that of potatoes, 140 per cent in vetch, and 300 per cent in that of the field pea, to 733 per cent in the case of rape.'

From among many reports received from practical earthworm culturists, I give part of a letter from a Georgia farmer, Mr. R. A. Caldwell:

'I have planted Moss Rose in experimental pots, same age and condition, one pot with worms, one without; invariably, the one with the worms will take on a new zest and life, and I have had them make such wonderful growth as 16 to 1. I have also grown petunias in boxes, in such size and profusion as to be unbelievable to one who never had a demonstration of the earthworm's fertilizing and cultivating ability. Petunias in soil of identical fertility, with the aid of hundreds of earthworms burrowing about their roots, produced leaves 1¼ to 1¾ inches wide by 3 inches long, while those in the boxes, without worms were yet ½ inch wide by 1 to 1¼ inches long; and the worm-fertilized plants were several times as tall as the others.'

In a full-column article entitled 'Earthworms in Role of Great Benefactors of the Human Race', Mr. W. A. Anderson, Editor of the *South Pasadena Review*, reported a number of growth experiments by the author.[2] One of the experiments reported on was this: We planted three boxes of lawn grass (*poa trivialis*). One box of good native soil as control; one box of identical soil, but with earthworms added; one box of pure earthworm castings. After germination and sixty days' growth, the grass was harvested and the results carefully compared. All

[1] Pages 158–9.
[2] *South Pasadena* (California) *Review*, 12th April 1940.

29

boxes produced good crops of grass. The box of native soil, with earthworms added, yielded 271 per cent more than the control box without worms. The box of earthworm castings yielded 463 per cent more than the control box without earthworms.

While one could give an endless array of reports similar to the above, I feel that the foregoing is amply sufficient to call attention to the fact that earthworms not only produce a great volume of topsoil, but they produce soil of unsurpassed fertility.

SUBSOIL: ITS TRANSLOCATION AND MIXING BY EARTHWORMS

On the subject of plant food in subsoil, we quote from *Productive Soils: The Fundamentals of Successful Soil Management and Profitable Crop Management*,[1] by Wilbur Walter Weir (B.S.[A], M.S., Ph.D., Forest Ecologist, Branch of Research, Forest Service, U.S. Dept. of Agriculture; one-time Soil Technologist, Bureau of Chemistry and Soils, University of Wisconsin):

'Subsoils contain plant food elements. It is important to bear in mind that subsoils also contain the important elements. In general, the surface soil contains more nitrogen than the subsoil, owing to the presence of more organic matter. Some deep, black soils may have as high a percentage of nitrogen in the subsoil (to a limited depth) as is contained in the surface stratum.

'The percentage of phosphorus in the surface layer is commonly greater than or equal to that contained in the subsoil. There is often a close relationship between the phosphorus and the amount of organic matter in mineral soils. This accounts for the higher phosphorus content of the upper strata. . . . On exhaustive cropping, the higher content of the surface soil is gradually reduced, until it equals at least the percentage contained in the subsoil.

'The potassium content is usually greater in the subsoils, especially when they are fine-textured. More potassium is found in subsoils of humid climates because of the presence of more fine particles, which are not only richer in potassium than the

[1] Pages 71 and 72.

coarser surface particles, but which absorb much more of the potassium leached down from the surface stratum.

'In arid and semi-arid soils, the phosphorus and potassium content of the surface soil is very much the same as that of the subsoil.'

From the foregoing quotation, it is readily appreciated what a great change may be made in the surface soil by the translocation of the subsoil to the top layers through the action of earthworms, especially when they are present in large numbers. The further importance of this soil movement from the depths to the top will be more fully understood in the light of the chemical changes the soil undergoes in its passage through the earthworm, which render it immediately available for the growing crops.

Every farmer and student of the soil knows that he cannot mix his topsoil with any great quantity of subsoil, without seriously reducing the fertility of the topsoil for immediate cropping. When subsoils are brought to the surface, especially from depths ranging from eighteen inches to two feet downward, they should be 'weathered' for months and mixed sparingly into the topsoil before they become fully available for best results. However, in the translocation of the subsoil by earthworms, the necessity for leaving the land fallow for months of weathering is avoided. The soil undergoes the necessary changes in the alimentary canals of the earthworms, preparing it, as has been stated, for immediate use.

The earthworms do not simply swallow the subsoil, bring it to the surface and deposit it. It is thoroughly mixed with the surface topsoil, so that the whole becomes one uniform, homogenized layer. To determine, as well as to illustrate, the mixing action of the earthworms, I prepared a culture box of carefully stratified layers of materials. Layers of granulated peat moss, mixed horse manure, rabbit manure, and chicken manure, with layers of good topsoil, were alternated. I then added several hundred earthworms on top of the stratified compost, allowing them to burrow down into the mix. After four months, I dumped the box for examination, I found no sign of stratification, the entire contents of the box having been converted into one homogenized mixture of fine, crumbly soil.

THE EARTHWORM AND ITS ENVIRONMENT

In my lath house, where I had established my experimental culture beds, great numbers of earthworms had burrowed into the earth from the culture boxes and other beds. I was using an old cement-mixing box for compost mixing. This box is about five feet long, thirty inches wide and twelve inches deep, with a galvanized iron bottom that had finally rusted into many holes. This box had been filled with rabbit manure and thoroughly wetted down, preparatory to mixing earthworm compost. However, I had neglected the task of mixing compost for a period of several weeks. Upon examination of the manure, I found that many earthworms had moved into the box from the damp earth beneath it and were producing many egg-capsules. I decided to leave the box and observe results, meantime covering it for protection against the summer sun and keeping the contents moist. The contents of the box soon lost identity as manure and after a few months, were found to have been completely converted into fine, dark, crumbly earth. I used this earthworm soil for a Victory Garden, grown in lug boxes, which supplied the table with lettuce, radishes, young onions, beets, and other greens of unusual excellence from early spring until late in the autumn. In this instance, the worms brought up considerable quantities of the subsoil from beneath the old cement box and thoroughly mixed and combined it with the rabbit manure, providing us with highly fertile and productive earth for our lug box garden.

In the Record of the U.S. Dept. of Agriculture Experiment Station, Vol. XVII, No. 8,[1] I find the following summary of an experiment by A. Murinov:

'Alternate layers of different kinds of soil were placed in zinc boxes with one glass side, earthworms were added, the soil kept in a proper state of moisture, and the changes which the soil underwent determined by analyses at the beginning and end of the experiments, which lasted one year. A check series of boxes were treated in the same manner, except that earthworms were not added.

'The results show that in the soils to which the earthworms were added the phosphoric acid soluble in 10 per cent hydro-

[1] Page 744.

chloric acid increased in all cases. The lime content, which at the beginning was greatest in the surface soils, was found at the end of the experiments to gradually increase from the surface towards the subsoils. The nitrogen was more uniformly distributed throughout the soil at the end of the experiment than at the beginning.'

In considering soil that has been worked over by earthworms and mixed with earthworm castings, attention should be called to the fact that the major plant-food elements—nitrogen, phosphorus and potassium—as well as the minor elements are intimately mixed and compounded with a high percentage of organic material, all in a finely divided state, which exposes many surfaces to the bacterial action so important in the topsoil. The earthworms 'sweeten' the soil, as the castings are rich in calcium carbonate that has been secreted from the blood of the earthworm in the metabolic processes and is then excreted in the castings.

Of particular note is the highly important fact that earthworm castings are very rich in nitrogen and may contain three times as much nitrogen as is found in the soil in which the worms work. This point is brought about by Horace Edward Stockbridge (Ph.D., Florida Agricultural College) in his book *Rocks and Soils: Their Origin, Composition and Characteristics*. In discussing earthworm castings, he says:

'. . . The amount of organic matter thus directly or indirectly added to the soil may be inferred from the fact that Darwin estimates that the material annually brought to the surface by worms is two-tenths of an inch per acre; equivalent to an average of 10·59 tons for each acre inhabited by worms. . . .

'Darwin states the ammonia content of worm castings to be 0·018 per cent, while the average ammonia present in common surface soils, as determined by Knop and Wolff, is only 0·00056 per cent. It therefore appears that the action of the worms has increased the ammonia content of the soil acted upon more than threefold (321 per cent).'

When given in the number of pounds per acre represented by 0·018 per cent of 10·59 tons, the amount of dry material which Darwin estimated annually passed through the earth-

D   33

worms of England per acre, the yearly accession of ammonia per acre is equivalent to 381·24 pounds. Ammonia is but one, and perhaps not the most important, of the constituents made available in the topsoil by the life-functions of earthworms. Quoting further from Dr. Stockbridge, 'This, be it borne in mind, is but a change wrought in one year and capable of yearly repetition. And, moreover, the entire mass of mould on every field passes in the course of a few years through their alimentary canals.'

In considering the significance of the above quotations and comments, it becomes apparent that in the example given of the action of the earthworms in the Anglo-Egyptian Sudan, the accession of ammonia to the topsoil would be an almost unbelievable amount. We can only surmise at this point that the accession of other plant food elements to the topsoil is proportional to the gain in nitrogen derived from ammonia.

The constant translocation of the plant food minerals from the subsoil to the surface zones, the thorough and ceaseless mixing of these elements with the soil, making it a finely conditioned evenly balanced soil without the necessity for long weathering, is just part of the important work of worms. Without quoting long references and details, let us summarize in part the work of earthworms in nature, with some related points, before passing on to the second part of the book, which deals with the controlled activity of earthworms.

SUMMARY

Earthworms are found in nature, ranging from a sparse population of a few thousand per acre to several millions per acre in favourable environment. They are distributed practically all over the globe.

While earthworms inhabit the surface layers of soil, deriving nutrition from the organic content of the soil, by swallowing the soil with all that it contains, they commonly burrow deep into the earth, riddling and honeycombing the earth to a depth of several feet. They come to the top to deposit their castings on top of the earth and in the loose surface layers, bringing the subsoil to the top and mixing it with the surface soil. In its passage through the worm, the mineral subsoil undergoes chemical changes, making it immediately available for plant nutrition. The aerating tunnels have the important function of greatly increasing the air capacity of the soil. In some cases the air capacity is increased as much as 60 to 75 per cent. Water penetration is improved where there is adequate earthworm population. Plough sole is eliminated. The rainfall is quickly absorbed, instead of running off or standing on the surface.

Wormcasts in acid soil are much less acid than the soil from which they are derived, the reduction in acidity in some instances amounting to as much as 75 per cent. In large numbers, the earthworms produce a topsoil that is practically a neutral humus. Also, earthworms reduce the alkalinity of the soil, so that alkaline soils are rendered less alkaline, while acid soils are rendered less acid.

Wormcasts commonly contain a high percentage of carbonates as well as a high percentage of nitrogen.

Earthworms increase the organic content of the surface soils by concentrating the organic content of the soil in the top layers Colloid humus is increased in the topsoil.

Bacterial multiplication and functioning are favoured by the action of earthworms. Where there are numerous earthworms, the soil also has a greatly increased number of soil bacteria, especially those concerned in the decomposition of cellulose. Decomposition of vegetable matter is much more rapid under the influence of earthworms.

Earthworms continually restore the plant food elements to the surface soils from the subsoils, thus overcoming the effects of leaching. Through the action of the earthworms, the potential fertility of the soil is rendered available by the fact that in the digestive processes of the earthworm the elements of plant nutrition are made water-soluble.

Earthworm castings have much greater productive value for plant growth than other soil, due to the fact that the nutritional elements have been concentrated in the castings in water-soluble form and in a more balanced condition. It is very much like feeding an animal with a well-balanced food ration, which is the ideal ration. The same applies to plant nutrition.

Resistance to pests and plant diseases is increased by action of earthworms, doubtless due to the production of a more balanced soil without deficiencies such as are found in soils dependent on chemical fertilization. Another important observation made, confirmed by numerous reports from earthworm culturists, is that fruit trees which have never borne fruit become productive after earthworms have been established around them. Undetermined deficiencies in the soil have evidently been remedied by the addition of earthworms, resulting in unproductive trees becoming fruitful.

In the second part of this book, many of the above points will be emphasized.

IV

CAN IT BE DONE?

In the foregoing pages I have discussed the earthworm in nature and shown something of its value in the soil. I have shown earthworms working in the soils of England in concentrations of from 25,000 to 53,000 per acre or more; and in the soils of the United States in concentrations of from 250,000 to upwards of 2,000,000 per acre. I have shown earthworms in England in an annual production of ten tons of castings per acre, while in the more favourable environment of the Upper Nile Valley I have reported on the annual production of more than two hundred tons of castings per acre.

The value of the earthworm in nature has been established beyond question. However, talking and writing about the value of earthworms in nature without doing anything about it is exactly like the academic discussion of water power in nature, without ever a thought or effort to utilize it in the service of man. The positive and unqualified answer to the question 'Can it be done?' is 'Yes—it has been done.'

One million earthworms per acre in good native soil is considered a very numerous natural population. Such a population represents approximately ten worms per cubic foot of soil, figuring an average working depth of thirty inches.

In the intensive propagation and use of domesticated earthworms, I have put them to work in controlled soil-building operations in concentrations of three thousand or more per cubic foot of composted parent material. In round numbers, such a concentration means *one hundred and thirty million worms* per acre-foot. The fact which makes such high concentrations possible is that *the number of earthworms in a given environmental space is limited only by the amount of available food present.* Lest the reader at this point be misled into thinking that three thousand earthworms could survive and work in a cubic foot of native soil, I hasten to state that in intensive propagation I provide the necessary concentrated nutritional material for the worms to work with in special culture beds or compost heaps.

I have gone to the greatest of all teachers—Mother Nature —for an example of 'mass-production' of earthworm topsoil in the Nile Valley, showing that it can be done. Not only does nature show that it can be done, but she shows how to do it. Making practical application of the lessons of nature, in the intensive propagation and use of domesticated earthworms we create a favourable environment, provide the abundant soil-building food of worms which is cheaply available practically everywhere, and the example of nature is duplicated in proportion to the amount of material and number of worms involved.

We now pass to the second part of the book, which deals more particularly with earthworms under controlled propagation and use.

PART TWO

THE EARTHWORM UNDER CONTROL

V

A NEW CONCEPT

In the following chapters I shall deal with the intensive propagation and use of earthworms under controlled environment. As has been stated, the one fact which makes it possible to utilize the earthworm in mass-production of humus-laden topsoil is that the number of earthworms in a given environment is limited only by the amount of available food present.

There are two objectives to be held in mind: The first is the most effective and economical utilization of all possible organic material, such as every form of vegetation, all animal manures, garbage, garden, orchard, and farm waste, and litter of all kinds; in fact, what we have termed the biological end-products of life as opposed to purely chemical end-products and strictly chemical fertilizers. The second objective is to establish the greatest possible earthworm population in the soil, using methods of tillage and organic fertilization that will favour the maintenance of earthworms in the soil, as well as the bacterial population that is concerned in soil-building and maintenance of the highest state of fertility in a permanent agriculture.

In propagating earthworms intensively in special culture beds, we use them very much as we use bacterial cultures, breeding them in high concentrations by furnishing adequate food material to support vast numbers in a limited area. Fertile farm and garden soil, properly handled through organic methods, will easily support from one to two million or more earthworms per acre-foot. Such a population will provide ideal aeration and air capacity for the soil, with good drainage, rapid water penetration and maximum moisture-holding capacity. At the same time, such an earthworm population provides a soil turnover and conditioning of upwards of two hundred tons of material annually, mixed and prepared in the humus mill of the earthworm and delivered to the root-zone of vegetation comprised in

41

the immediate six to eighteen inches of surface soil. In special culture beds, we commonly propagate earthworms in concentrations of upwards of *three thousand* worms per cubic foot of material, which means, in round numbers, *one hundred and thirty million* worms per acre-foot.

With the above figures and objectives in mind, it is possible to begin to visualize the possibilities of soil-building, whether it be for a single flower-pot, a window-box of flowers, a small city yard or garden, or more extensive acreage in large gardens, nurseries, orchards, or farms.

We ordinarily think of earthworms as small, wriggling, insignificant, repugnant creatures. To appreciate properly the possibilities inherent in the intensive propagation and use of worms in soil-building, we should gain a new and different concept, thinking of them in units of hundreds, thousands, or even millions, instead of thinking in terms of separate, tiny, individual worms. For purposes of illustration, suppose we ask, 'How many are a million earthworms?' and use our imagination in answering the question.

Mentally, we shall combine one million earthworms into a single, composite animal and place this animal on an acre of ground, with a year's ration of fertile topsoil piled up around it in symmetrical piles for its daily consumption. We shall then have a monster animal, weighing more than 2,000 pounds, with 365 piles of soil before it. Each pile will contain approximately one cubic yard of earth, weighing upwards of 2,000 pounds. Each pile will represent the daily ration of this fantastic, dirt-eating animal, that will swallow its own weight or more of earth each day of the year. Such will be our composite animal, mentally integrated from one million earthworms. Now let us check with the facts, as they have been established by careful experiment.

I have weighed many of the earthworms propagated during my research. On the average, they run about 500 to the pound, or about 31 worms per ounce. The fully mature worm, in good condition, averages four inches in length. Thus we find that one million of them would weigh 2,000 pounds. If placed end to end, they would make a continuous line over 6¼ miles long. An individual worm, eating its way through the soil, will swallow its own weight of earth daily, in order to absorb from the soil the infinitesimal amount of nutrition required to keep a worm in good condition. When we analyse and carefully study these figures, we begin to gain a concept of the tremendous soil-building force which is at work in the earth when it is populated by one million earthworms per acre. The earthworm is just as truly an air-breathing, manure-producing animal as a horse, cow, or other domestic animal. The difference is that earthworms work unseen and their manure is so thoroughly combined with the soil that it cannot be separated. In fact, as has been pointed out, the manure of the earthworm *is* finely conditioned soil.

At first thought, when it is stated that an earthworm will ingest its own weight in soil each twenty-four hours, this amount seems almost unbelievable. However, when the eating and excretory activities of the chicken are compared with those of the earthworm, a ration of topsoil equal to the weight of the earthworm each day seems a very reasonable amount. On the average, a mature hen will drop seventy-five pounds of manure each year. Chickens utilize only about 10 per cent of the nutritional value of the food they eat, the balance going out in their droppings. Thus they have to gorge many hours each day in order to produce eggs in commercially profitable numbers. Suppose that a laying hen had to swallow enough earth daily to secure the amount of organic food necessary to keep her in good laying condition, instead of feeding on concentrated grains and mashes. To do this, she would have to consume several times her own weight of earth each day, assuming that her digestive organs were similar to those of the earthworm. Yet that is exactly what the earthworm has to do. The earthworm lives on the organic content of the soil, which it swallows with all that is contained therein. The earthworm is so constructed as to be able to digest this material, thus gaining the small amount of food necessary for nutrition. Only because it is perhaps the most perfect digestive organism known to the animal world is the earthworm able to absorb enough food from an amount of earth equal to its own weight to maintain it in a fat and active condition. Thus, the statement that the earthworm swallows its own weight of earth daily appears, on examination, perfectly reasonable and understandable.

I again repeat: Think of earthworms in large units of hundreds, thousands, millions; for in intensive propagation and use of earthworms we must deal with great numbers of them. Otherwise, we cannot expect to attain results worthy of consideration.

VI

EARTHWORMS IN GENERAL FARMING

One of the questions most frequently asked is 'How would you utilize earthworms for large acreage and general farming?' We are fortunate in having a true story of a large Ohio farm which was operated with full use of earthworms during the period from about 1830 to 1890. Early in my research into the subject of earthworms, I came in contact with the late Dr. George Sheffield Oliver, pioneer earthworm culturist of California. We were close friends and collaborators for a number of years prior to his death. In answer to my questions about the use of earthworms for large acreage, Dr. Oliver related to me the story of his early youth on his grandfather's farm. I can think of no better way to present the technique for utilization of earthworms in general farming and for large acreage than to tell the story, reconstructing it very much as Dr. Oliver told it.

While this story gives the broad basic principles for use of earthworms in general farming, the earthworm farmer of to-day will have the advantage of modern composting techniques and many other improvements which have been worked out during the past few decades. However, the earthworms remain the same, for they have come down to us practically unchanged, from remote geological ages to the present.

In a later chapter, I shall give a report of earthworm tillage on a modern farm, with results which are corroborative of those reported as follows by Dr. Oliver.

MY GRANDFATHER'S EARTHWORM FARM

The story of a self-contained farm of 160 acres, maintained in ever-increasing fertility over a period of more than sixty years, through the utilization of earthworms. A true story related to the author by the late Dr. George Sheffield Oliver.

When, as a small boy, I went to live with my grandfather,

45

THE EARTHWORM UNDER CONTROL

George Sheffield, in northern Ohio, I found him living on a model farm of 160 acres, which he had farmed continuously for more than sixty years. He was a man who loved the soil and took pride in every detail of his farm. I remember him as a tall, striking figure, of the type of Edwin Markham. In fact, in later years, when I came across a picture of the poet Markham, I was struck by the close resemblance of the two men— their features were almost identical and they could have easily been taken for twins.

Some of my pleasantest memories from the period of several years which I spent on this farm are the daily horseback rides I took with my grandfather. After all these years I can still see him, at the age of seventy-five, riding with the ease and grace of the practised horseman, swinging into the saddle with the facility of a man in his prime. At that age he still took delight in riding the young three-year-olds. He lived to the ripe old age of ninety-three.

Originally, this farm-holding had been 1,800 acres, but it had been sold off in forty-acre tracts to former tenants until there remained only the farmstead of 160 acres. It had been my grandfather's practice to select young single men as farm help. As these men reached maturity and married and wanted to establish homes of their own, my grandfather would set each of them up on a tract of forty acres or more, assist them in getting started, and accept a payment contract over a period of forty years. Thus, his close neighbours were men who, like himself, loved the soil and could co-operate in all community work. My grandfather often remarked that he was making more profit from his remaining 160 acres than he ever made on the original 1,800 acres, due to his lifetime experience, improved methods, and the intensive utilization of earthworms.

The homestead was located at the centre of the farm. Four acres of orchard and garden furnished an abundance of fruits and vegetables the year round. Root cellars, vegetable banks, canned and dried fruits and vegetables provided for the winter months. The house and orchard were backed by forty acres of timbered land—maple, hickory, black walnut, burr oak, and many other trees native to Ohio. Incidentally, the farm was fenced with black walnut rails—beautiful timber which would be almost priceless at this time. My grandfather called this timbered tract his park. It was, indeed, a wonderful park, abounding in small game and bird life to delight the soul of a small boy with his first gun. The park was well watered with living springs and a quite generous-sized creek ran through it, large enough to furnish all the fish the family needed. I was designated as the official fish-catcher, a task which I dearly loved.

It is important to get a picture of the lay-out of the farm, in order to understand its efficient operation without waste of time and energy. It was divided into four tracts of forty acres each. The homestead, with orchard, garden and park occupied one forty. Near the centre of the 160 acres was located the great barnyard of about two acres, with broad swinging gates in each of the four sides, opening into lanes which led into each of the forty-acre tracts. Thus the stock could be herded into any part of the farm, simply by opening the proper gate and driving them through the lane into the particular section that was to be pastured.

Located in the four corners of the barnyard were the straw-stacks—alternating wheat stack, oat stack, wheat stack, oat stack. These stacks occupied permanent raised platforms, about six feet above the ground, resting on sturdy walnut posts and covered by small logs, or poles, cut from the woods. The stock had good shelter under these platforms in the winter, feeding on the straw overhead through the cracks between the logs. Plenty of straw was always thrown down for bedding. My grandfather claimed that each kind of straw added valuable elements of fertility to his compost, and he alternated the straw stacks so that the wheat and oat straw would be evenly mixed.

In the centre of the barnyard was the compost pit, which, in the light of my present knowledge, I now know to have been the most perfect and scientific fertilizer production unit I have ever known. This pit was fifty feet wide and one hundred feet long and had been excavated to a depth of about two feet. At each end, evenly spaced from side to side and about twenty feet from the end, a heavy log post was deeply anchored. These posts were probably twelve to fifteen feet high, with an overhead cable anchored to the top of each post and running to the barn. On these cables were large travelling dump baskets, in which the manure from the barn was transported to the compost pit and dumped each morning, to be evenly spread in a uniform layer. By means of the posts in each end, the manure could be dumped at a spot most convenient for proper handling. With this arrangement of overhead trolley from barn to compost pit, it was possible to clear the barn quickly each morning of the night's droppings and spread the material in the pit without any loss of the valuable elements of fresh manure. This is an important point in the utilization of earthworms for general farming.

Just outside the barnyard ran the creek, which found its source in a big spring in the park. From this creek an abundance of water was piped by gravity into the watering troughs for the stock in barn and yard. Also a flume, with a controlled intake, led to the compost pit, so that when necessary the compost could be well soaked in a few minutes. The homestead occupied ground on a higher level than the barnyard, so that drainage was always away from the house and there was no chance of pollution from the teeming life of the barnyard.

To one side of the barnyard and at a higher level than the floor of the yard was located the ice pond. This pond was so arranged that it could be filled from a flume, leading by gravity from the creek at one end, while at the lower end a spillway was provided so that the pond could be drained. At the proper season, the ice pond would be filled and when the ice formed to the right thickness the annual harvest of ice was cut and stored in the ice house, to provide an abundance of ice for all purposes the year round. The bottom of this pond was formed of a fine-textured red clay. Each spring the pond was drained and with teams of scrapers many tons of this clay were scraped out and diked around the borders of the pond to weather for use on the compost heap.

And now enters the earthworm. For more than sixty years these 160 acres had been farmed without a single crop failure. My grandfather was known far and wide for the unequalled excellence of his corn and other grain, and a large part of his

(a)

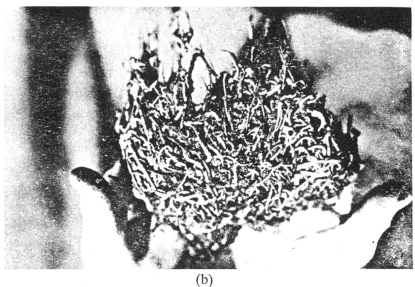

(b)

PLATE IV. (a) Earthworm culture in lug boxes; (b) A double-handful of domesticated earthworms

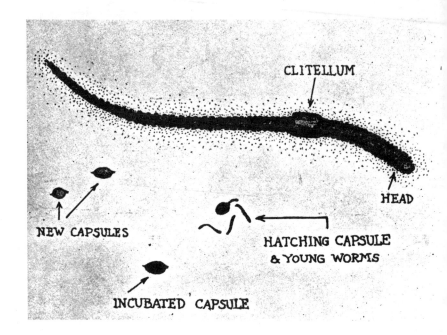

PLATE III. Egg-capsules
(*Earthmaster Farms, Roscoe, California*)

surplus was disposed of at top prices for seed purposes. The farm combined general farming and stock raising; my grandfather's hobby, for pleasure and profit, was the breeding and training of fine saddle horses and matched Hambletonian teams. He maintained a herd of about fifty horses, including stud, brood mares, and colts in all stages of development. In addition to horses, he had cattle, sheep, hogs, and a variety of fowl, including a flock of about five hundred chickens which had the run of the barnyard, with a flock of ducks. Usually about three hundred head of stock were wintered. The hired help consisted of three or four men, according to the season, with additional help at rush seasons. This establishment was maintained in prosperity and plenty, and my grandfather attributed his unvarying success as a farmer to his utilization of earthworms in maintaining and rebuilding the fertility of the soil in an unbroken cycle. The heart of the farming technique was the compost pit.

As previously mentioned, the pit was fifty by one hundred feet, excavated to a depth of two feet, and it was especially designed to provide a great breeding bed for earthworms. Literally millions of earthworms inhabited the pit and compost heap. Each morning the barn was cleaned, the droppings for the previous twenty-four hours were transported to the heap by the dump baskets on the overhead trolley, and evenly spread over the surface. The building of the compost heap was an invariable daily routine of the farm work. A flock of chickens everlastingly scratched and worked in the barnyard, assisted by the ducks, gleaning every bit of undigested grain that found its way into the manure, and incidentally adding about twenty tons of droppings per year to the material which eventually found its way into the compost heap. The cattle and sheep grazed around the four straw stacks and bedded under the shelter of the stacks, adding their droppings to the surface and treading them into the bedding material. From time to time the entire barnyard was raked and scraped, the combined manure and litter being harrowed to the compost heap and distributed in an even layer over the entire surface. As the compost reached a depth of twelve to fourteen inches, several tons of the red clay from the border of the ice pond would be hauled in and spread in an even layer over the surface of the compost. Thus the variety of animal manures from horses, cattle, sheep, pigs, and fowl alternated in the heap with layers of the fine-textured clay, rich in mineral elements. Meantime, beneath the surface the earthworms multiplied in untold millions, gorging ceaselessly upon the manures and decomposing vegetable matter, as well as the mineral clay soil, and depositing their excreta in the form of castings—a completely broken down, deodorized soil, rich in all the elements of plant life. From time to time as necessary (the necessity being determined by careful inspection on the part of my grandfather), the compost would be watered through the flume leading from the creek, thus being provided with the moisture needed to permit the earthworms to function to the greatest advantage in their life-work of converting compost to humus.

Within a few months the earthworms had completed their work. When spring arrived, the season of the annual ploughing, the top layer of the heap would be stripped back, revealing the perfect work of the worms. What had originally been an ill-smelling mixture of manure, urine, and litter, was now a dark, fertile, crumbly soil, with the odour of fresh-turned earth. This material was not handled with forks, but with shovels. There were no dense cakes of burned, half-decomposed manure. My grandfather would take a handful of the material and smell it before pronouncing it ready for the fields. The 'smell test' was a sure way of judging the quality. When perfect transformation had taken place, all odour of manure had disappeared and the material had the clean smell of new earth.

At this time of the year, the beginning of the spring ploughing, the compost heap was almost a solid mass of earthworms and every shovel of material would contain scores of them. As I now know from years of study and experiment, every cubic foot of this material contained hundreds and hundreds of earthworm egg-capsules, each of which, within two or three weeks after burial in the fields, would hatch out from two or three to as many as twenty worms. Thus the newly hatched earthworms became the permanent population of the soil, following their life-work of digesting the organic material, mixing and combining it with much earth in the process, and depositing it in and on the surface as castings—a finely conditioned, homogenized soil, rich in the stored and available elements of plant food in water-soluble form.

When the spring ploughing began, the following method was adopted : Several teams were used with the ploughs, while two or three farm wagons with deep beds were employed in hauling the crumbly end-product of the earthworms from the compost pit to the fields. The wagons worked ahead of the ploughs, the material being spread generously on the surface and quickly ploughed under. Seldom was any material exposed on the surface more than a few minutes ahead of the ploughs, for part of the technique followed was to plough the egg-capsules and live earthworms under, so that as many of the earthworms would survive as possible to continue their valuable work in the soil. Also it was necessary to plough the worms and capsules under as quickly as possible to escape the voracious, marauding crows which swarmed in great flocks to the feast of worms and capsules so thoughtfully spread for them. At this time, to my great delight, I was appointed crow hunter. Armed with a light shotgun, I industriously banged away at the crows to my heart's content, killing some of them and keeping hundreds of them at a distance until the ploughs could turn the earth and bury the worms and capsules safe from the birds and the sun. I estimate that several tons per acre of this highly potent fertilizer material were annually ploughed into the fields in preparation for the crops to follow. On account of this technique, not only was the earth continually occupied by a very numerous worm population the year round, but annually a generous 'seeding' with live earthworms and capsules was planted to replenish and help renew the fertility of the earth.

More than forty years after my experience on my grandfather's farm, studies of the earthworms in the soil of Ohio were made by the Ohio State University. In plots of soil covered with bluegrass, on the Ohio State University Farm, they found earthworms in numbers of one million or more per acre. From my experience of almost a lifetime of study and experimentation with earthworms, I am sure that the earthworm population of my grandfather's farm far exceeded one million to the acre.

In the annual distribution of the fertilizer, my grandfather never completely stripped the compost pit. One year he would begin the hauling at one end of the pit, stripping back the top layers of material which had not been broken down, leaving a generous portion at the other end of the pit as breeding and culture ground. After the hauling of the fertilizer was completed, the entire remaining contents of the pit were evenly spread over the entire surface for 'mother substance' and the new compost heap was thus begun. By this method there was always left a very large number of breeding earthworms, with vast numbers of egg capsules, to repopulate the compost pit and carry on the highly important work of providing fertilizer for the coming year. In this warm, highly favourable environment, the worms multiplied with maximum rapidity.

In my experiments in later years, I determined that certain breeds of earthworms, in a favourable environment and with an abundance of food material to work on, will work ceaselessly in concentrations of more than 50,000 to the cubic yard; also, that 50,000 earthworms thus working will completely transform one cubic yard of material per month. Thus, in nature we have a constructive force which creates humus with amazing rapidity when given the opportunity and, under proper control, furnishes a method for utilizing every possible end-product of biological activity through the very simple process of composting with earthworms.

Going back to my grandfather's farm, his regular rotation of crops was corn, wheat, oats, timothy, and clover hay, in a three-year cycle. One forty-acre tract was planted to timothy and clover each year. A crop of hay was harvested and stored for the winter, the field was used for grazing, and finally a crop was turned under for green manure. In this manner, each year one 'forty' was left undisturbed by the plough for a number of months, allowing the earthworm population to work and multiply to the maximum, while converting the organic content of the earth into the finest form of humus. When the clover fields were ploughed under an almost unbelievable number of earth-worms was revealed as the sod was turned.

One fact I failed to mention was that this land was not usually considered the finest to begin with. It was a thin top-soil, only six to eight inches in depth over much of the farm, underlaid by limestone. On account of the shallow depth of the soil, deep subsoil ploughing was not possible. I well remember how the ploughs would scoot along on top of the almost surface limestone layer. However, the vast earthworm population pene-trated deeply into the subsoil and constantly brought up parent mineral material to combine with the surface soil, which made up for the lack of deep soil. My grandfather often remarked that in all his sixty years of farming he had never had a crop failure. His corn was the finest in all the country and was eagerly sought for seed. He also originated a sweet corn, of a delicious flavour, which was very highly esteemed throughout that section and was known at that time as 'Sheffield corn'. The ears were very uniform and evenly filled to the end, and I re-member that the cob of this special corn was hardly larger than a carpenter's lead pencil. My grandfather never sold this corn, · but reserved it to give to friends who came from far and wide for the prized seed and even wrote to him from distant points for seed.

Now looking back through the long vista of years to the method practised on my grandfather's farm, in the light of my own experience as well as the experience of a host of others, I am struck by the reflection that here was a simple farmer, working without any specialized knowledge of earthworms to begin with, long before Charles Darwin's famous book on *The Formation of Vegetable Mould* appeared; and yet, in an in-tensely practical way, utilizing all that Darwin later revealed in his great book, but with the exception that Darwin never sug-gested the 'harnessing of the earthworm' for intensive human use. Darwin's classic study only emphasized the importance of the work of the earthworm in nature, with no practical applica-tion to the personal agricultural problems of man.

Before ending this narrative of my grandfather's earthworm farm, I must mention the orchard, the garden, and the fence rows. The fence rows throughout the farm were planted to a great variety of fruit trees, which were allowed to develop from seedlings. Particularly do I remember the cherry trees, some of them fifty feet high and each tree bearing a different kind of fruit. In the four acres of orchard and garden surrounding the house there was produced a great variety of fruit, furnishing an abundance, in season, for the family as well as for many of the neighbours. In those days the fruit was not sold. I remember an often-repeated remark of my grandfather upon the care of trees, especially fruit trees. He said, 'Never disturb the soil under a tree. The earthworm is the best plough for a tree and I do not want them disturbed.' The vegetable garden was especially fine, kept wonderfully enriched from the compost pit, the soil being literally alive with earthworms. A profusion of flowers both potted and otherwise, as well as a wealth of shrubbery, beautified the place. For choice flowers, we would use a rich mixture of fine soil and material from the compost pit.

My grandfather's earthworm farm furnishes an example of the technique for utilizing the earthworm in general farming operations, either on a large or small scale. From my observations as a small boy, supplemented by much friendly and loving instruction from my grandfather on the subject of earthworms, and from more than forty years' experience in my own work, I am fully convinced that the harnessing of the earthworm will be one of the major factors in the eventual salvation of the soil. I know that the soil can be made to produce several times as much as the present average, through the utilization of the earthworm.

VII

ORCHARDING WITH EARTHWORMS

In the story of 'My Grandfather's Earthworm Farm' George Sheffield is quoted as saying, in regard to the care of trees, 'Never disturb the soil under a tree. The earthworm is the best plough for taking care of a tree.' The wisdom of this remark is appreciated fully only when a study is made of the subject of orcharding. When we go to nature where primeval forests have stood for centuries, we find the ground riddled to great depth by earthworm burrows. Earthworms like to work in the shade, among the fine roots of trees, finding sustenance in the organic debris and bacterial life of the soil, in the dead bacteria as well as the products of bacterial life. Apart from vegetation, there is a vast world of unseen bacterial life in the soil, amounting in aggregate weight in the case of fertile agricultural lands to much more than all animal life which crawls, creeps, walks, runs, and flies on and above the surface of the ground. Because we do not see this microscopic universe, we may not visualize or sense its extent.

The multiplication of bacteria is so rapid that, starting with a single cell, under favourable conditions the numbers will reach astronomical figures within a few hours, with a bulk and weight of such magnitude that the human mind cannot grasp the total. The number of bacteria in an ounce of fertile topsoil is variously estimated as from eighteen million to twenty-four billion. When we consider that bacteria appear as dots under the microscope when magnified one thousand times, the results of such multiplication become still harder to grasp. If we were to magnify a man to one thousand times his size, he would appear more than one mile tall and a quarter-mile broad. On this point we shall quote from *Bacteria in Relation to Soil Fertility*,[1] by Dr.

[1] Page 26.

THE EARTHWORM UNDER CONTROL

Joseph E. Greaves (M.S., Ph.D., Professor of Bacteriology and Physiological Chemistry, Utah Agricultural College):

'A bacterial generation is taken as the time required for a mature cell to divide and the resulting daughter cells to reach maturity. This process may be completed in half an hour—at times even more rapidly. Under less favourable circumstances it may be much longer. It has been estimated that if bacterial multiplication went unchecked the descendants of one cell would in two days number 281,500,000,000, and that in three days the descendants of this single cell would weigh 148,356,000 pounds. It has been further estimated by an eminent biologist that if proper conditions could be maintained for their life activity, in less than five days they would make a mass which would completely fill as much space as is occupied by all the oceans on the earth's surface, if the water had an average depth of one mile.'

Lest some reader becomes alarmed about bacteria, let us state that they are self-limiting, the same as other life-forms, being strictly limited by the amount of food available in their environment. Also, the by-products of their own life-processes accumulate rapidly and, as it were, they are soon stewing in their own juice to their own destruction. Incidentally, it is doubtful whether, in the absence of the bacterial life of the soil, the higher forms of animal life could exist. Like the earthworm, bacteria are the unseen but ceaseless transformers of the end-products of life back to the soil in the eternal cycle—from earth, through life, back to earth.

The above may at first appear as a digression from the subject of orcharding. However, in considering the nutrition of trees through the aid of earthworms, it is important to understand fully the source of nutrition for the worms as well as for the trees. There is much more sustenance in the soil than may be derived from the gross forms of vegetation in and above the earth. So, in considering the life of a tree and its nutrition, it is well to examine the elements which enter into its growth and maintenance.

We stand in awed amazement as we contemplate a *Sequoia gigantea*, towering nearly three hundred feet into the air, bearing within its bulk trainloads of material, carrying concealed within its growth-rings its recorded age record of perhaps three to five thousand years. Where did it come from, how did it grow, from what hidden source does its mighty heart draw its inconceivable strength? No man has carried small bags of chemical fertilizer in a foolish attempt to help nourish this tree into its giant size. No man-made plough has disturbed the surface of the earth at its base. Yet here it stands, with a life-span reaching toward a geological age. We are reminded of the scriptural injunction, 'Consider the lilies, how they grow,' and might well paraphrase the line to read, 'Consider the trees, how they grow!'

When we come to orcharding with the aid of earthworms, we should not be too much concerned about fertilizers, or worry at all about cultivation. The thing to do is to offer a little friendly co-operation with nature, stand back, and watch the tree grow.

While the same principles apply to orcharding in general, my own studies of the earthworm in orcharding have been confined for the most part to citrus orcharding, by reason of the fact that I live in Southern California where citrus fruit is the main orcharding industry. Some time ago I visited the great orange-growing section around Riverside, California, the particular end of my journey being 'Hanford Loam', a grove which the owner, Mr. Frank Hinckley, has operated by the non-cultivation method for a period of more than twenty years. Mr. Hinckley is a hard-headed, successful orange grower and business man who has made money growing oranges. He has been growing oranges all his life and his experience covers a period of more than forty years. He is well educated, well informed, methodical, and practical; and, as he has kept careful records for many years, he has his data and knows what he is talking about. The ten-acre tract comprising Hanford Loam is one of the outstanding groves of the state. I was amazed at the size and luxuriance of the trees. Many of the leaves were of such unusual size as to be almost unbelievable when compared with the foliage of the average orange tree.

Mr. Hinckley's own story of his experience in developing

this grove conveys the facts in a most forceful manner. After my visit to his place, I wrote him a letter, requesting a report for my records. Under date of 17th October 1939, I received the following letter.

DEAR DOCTOR BARRETT,

I have your letter of October 10th and will try to give some information that will be of value in your research.

I might say that my experience with the earthworms is more on the practical side than on the experimental. On one of my ten-acre groves, Hanford Loam, I discontinued all cultivation about eighteen years ago. At that time the twenty-eight-year-old trees appeared to have reached their limit as to size and production, about three hundred boxes per acre per year.

The first year after changing my cultural method to one of non-cultivation, I noticed a great difference in water penetration. Plough sole was eliminated, the trees started growing, and they have continued to do so ever since, until now they are large, fine trees, and my production average for the last fifteen years has been about 630 boxes per acre per year.

Soon after I quit all cultivation, I noticed that the earthworms were doing a wonderful job of tilling the soil; they eliminated all plough sole, leaving the ground porous and mellow. I also perceived that they were feeding on the leaves that had accumulated in the furrows and around under the trees. Raking the leaves out from under the trees and placing them beneath the drip of the trees encouraged the worms to work that portion of the soil most, as it kept more moist. Under such ideal conditions, the earthworms rapidly increased until now they are able to work every foot of soil in my grove—in fact, I might say the soil is continually in motion. As the trees have a heavy foliage of large leaves, the leaf-drop seems to furnish ample food for the worms.

I have used a soluble commercial fertilizer, calcium nitrate or sulphate of ammonia, for the past twenty years, with the exception of one year when I used cottonseed meal. Until six years ago I averaged about $3\frac{1}{4}$ pounds of actual nitrogen per tree per year, but the last six years I have averaged $1\frac{1}{3}$ pounds of actual nitrogen per tree per year. There has been no organic matter added to this grove since the autumn of 1919. The quality of the fruit has been above the average; also the sizes have been in the desirable brackets. In my opinion, there is no doubt that the earthworms add fertility to the soil besides conditioning it.

I also have a twenty-acre grove in sandy soil, which I took care of in the mechanical way for fourteen years, and I saw very few worms in all that time. For the past fourteen years, however, I have applied my non-cultivation method, and the worms are increasing every year. They started at the lower end of the furrows, where the soil is heaviest; and as the soil changes from the accumulation of leaves around the trees, the worms are able to live and increase.

These groves are kept clean of weeds by hoeing; the furrows have become shallow and wide from hoeing and raking the leaves. The water can thus cover a larger area of the surface, making as much soil as possible available for the worms to use during the dry season, without extra expense.

I also have a lot of sixty-five orange trees at home, which I purchased a year ago. This soil is a heavy red soil and very subject to plough sole. I am well pleased with the way the worms have multiplied and eliminated the plough sole under my method within the year; and they will no doubt continue to better the soil and aid the trees.

In regard to the amount of water used, I find that since the worms have opened up the soil water penetrates more freely. I can irrigate in a much shorter time and with a larger volume of water per furrow. Under this method of non-cultivation, I use a little less water, but the trees are able to use more of that which is applied.

Our Deputy Farm Adviser is making a graph, consisting of the sizes, grades, and amounts of boxes covering the past twenty years. When I receive these data, I will be glad to send them to you if you so desire. Thank you for your interest in my work.

Very truly,
(*signed*) FRANK HINCKLEY.

THE EARTHWORM UNDER CONTROL

At the date of this writing, January of 1944, it is of interest to point out that Mr. Hinckley had eliminated the plough from his orcharding operations more than twenty years before the appearance of Edward H. Faulkner's book, *Plowman's Folly*, currently on its way to becoming a best-seller. Since receiving the above report from Mr. Hinckley, we have visited his place a number of times and a good many interesting details have been brought out, with many things not covered in his letter. One of the most astonishing statements was made by him in answer to our question, 'How much money do you have invested in machinery?' Mr. Hinckley replied: 'I have thirty acres in oranges in Hanford Loam and another grove near here. I believe my total investment in machinery is less than ten dollars, consisting of hoes and rakes. A near neighbour, with thirty-two acres of oranges, has over four thousand dollars' worth of machinery and hires an expert to operate it. I call in a Mexican boy every other month and we go over my groves with hoe and rake to eliminate the few weeds which come from seeds that are blown in by the wind.'

Mr. Hinckley stated that after the initial change from the old cultural methods, his labour costs were less. By use of the hoe promptly to eliminate weeds, never allowing them to go to seed, the orchard was soon practically free from weeds. No tractors or machines are required in the non-cultivation method; therefore the trees do not need to be trimmed high. In Mr. Hinckley's orchard the trees have been allowed to develop until the limbs practically touch the ground, maintaining a dense shade over the entire surface and an unfavourable environment for weeds. Also the shade conserves surface moisture and this favours the development of a large earthworm population.

In the case of Mr. Hinckley, there was no special propagation of earthworms. He simply created a favourable environment for the development of the native earthworm population, discontinued ploughing and breaking up their breeding grounds, provided cover for the worms in the form of leaf-drop raked underneath the drip of the tree, and the worms began to multiply. After a few years this grove has become one vast earthworm culture bed. At the time this chapter is written, Mr. Hinckley's orchard is over fifty years old and is in greater production than ever before, whereas at the time the new method was started the grove was twenty-eight years old and was not showing a profit. In fact, it was going back.

In orcharding with the aid of earthworms, a small, highly productive, long-lived orchard, with top quality fruit, lower labour costs, less fertilizer costs, and the practical elimination of culls, can be made to take the place of a much larger acreage under the generally accepted cultural methods. Through earthworm culture, young groves can be brought to profitable production in a much shorter period of time than by the old methods; and the life of a grove, with earthworms instead of ploughs, extends far beyond the life of a grove where the earthworms are constantly retarded in their development by frequent ploughing. And where heavy use of chemical fertilizers is the practice, the earthworm population may entirely disappear, and, in addition, the highly important bacterial life of the soil be inhibited.

The quickest method of developing earthworms in orchards is to establish generous colonies of 'domesticated earthworms' under each tree, with organic fertilization similar to that used on 'My Grandfather's Earthworm Farm'. By this method the proliferation of earthworms is accelerated many times beyond anything found in nature. Within a few months results may be obtained which would otherwise require years. Methods for intensive propagation of domesticated earthworms for all horticultural purposes will be taken up in later chapters.

Since becoming acquainted with Mr. Hinckley and his methods and results through 'earthworm tillage', we have had reports from a number of other orchardists. We will mention one small tract in particular, a five-acre grove near Costa Mesa, California. This grove is rated very highly by the citrus-growing people. It is handled by methods similar to Mr. Hinckley's grove; that is, methods which we have called 'earthworm tillage'. For the year 1945 the owner of this grove stated that he received a gross amount of $7,500 for his orange crop from these five acres. Examination shows that the entire tract is really a great earthworm culture bed. From a few such reports investigated,

61

we are led to conclude that the earthworm doubtless deserves credit for many of the outstanding results which have been observed in other successful orchards.

While we have discussed the earthworm in citrus orcharding, the same principles apply to other types of orcharding, as well as to general farming and production of food crops. What I wish to emphasize, regardless of vegetation under consideration, is that with earthworms and the other allied forces of nature, utilized properly, we obtain a soil with a maximum of plant nutrients in available form. From such soil, experience has shown that maximum production results are obtained, both in quantity and quality.

VIII

DOMESTICATED EARTHWORMS

In the unhurried processes of nature it may require from forty to fifty years for native earthworms to spread slowly from a single breeding colony and fully impregnate an acre of ground. In England, where the earthworms had been working in a fairly favourable environment through geological ages, Darwin found native earthworms in numbers ranging from 25,000 to 50,000 or more per acre in some soils, which means less than one worm per cubic foot of surface soil. Even in these small numbers, as has been pointed out, Darwin estimated that from ten to eighteen tons of dry material per acre passed through the bodies of earthworms in England each year to be deposited in and on the surface as castings.

I have previously mentioned the earthworms in the State of Ohio, where they have been found in bluegrass land in numbers upwards of a million per acre. If we figure an average working depth of thirty inches, one million worms per acre would mean, in round numbers, about ten worms per cubic foot. A population of two to four native earthworms per cubic foot in farm soil or other soil is considered a quite numerous earthworm population. In previous pages I have shown the almost incredible amount of cultivation and translocation of soil which earthworms perform under favourable conditions. In intensive propagation and use, we control the environment and create nutritional conditions which are most favourable to proliferation and grcwth of earthworms. We commonly develop culture beds with concentrations of as many as 3,000 worms per cubic foot, with corresponding results in the production of humus. To breed worms in such great numbers in limited space, we must of course provide food material and soil-building elements for them to work with. It should always be borne in mind that worms live on the organic contents of the soil. Therefore, if

63

the soil furnished them is deficient in organic material, the worms cannot live in it. They do not secure any nutrition from the purely mineral content of the soil, but only from the organic content that has been derived through life processes.

In the adaptation of the earthworm as a controlled servant of man, the elements of chance must be eliminated and results must be measured in units of time. While we may build soil for future generations, we want to have the benefit of the soil here and now, and this is the reason for intensive breeding of earthworms. Working with the sure methods of definite purpose and knowledge, we may achieve results within a few months which would otherwise require many decades to accomplish, were we to wait on the leisurely processes of nature, which take no account of time.

In using the term 'domesticated earthworm', I am referring to a breed of earthworms which has been developed and modified by selective breeding and feeding over a period of several years, to meet the requirements for intensive use in horticulture and agriculture. The original object of the experimental work which led to the development of the domesticated earthworm was to eliminate the elements of chance which are encountered in dealing with the exceedingly numerous varieties of native earthworms; to speed up results to meet the demands of practical people under all conditions and environments, both city and country; and, above all, to develop an earthworm which would be adaptable to every kind of soil and food and one which could be changed readily from one environment to another. The ordinary native earthworm is a slave to the environment into which it is born. It is hatched from the egg-capsule as a full-fledged earthworm and immediately begins its life-work of devouring the surrounding soil in search of sustenance. It grows to maturity on the available food present, and its chemical make-up adapts itself to the particular element in which it lives. Transfer the native earthworm to a different soil or food, and it will usually die, or at least require a long period of time to adapt itself and become prolific in the new location.

Another important consideration in earthworm culture is the question of fertility and proliferation. In some species, great numbers of infertile capsules are produced and only one or two worms will be hatched from the fertile capsule. In other species practically all the capsules are fertile, and each will hatch out from three or four to as high as twenty worms. Some species live and thrive only in a very limited range of soil acidity; in fact, must have an almost neutral soil to survive. Others will thrive and multiply in a very wide range of soil, from very acid to markedly alkaline. The serious importance of this point of soil acidity will be appreciated by those who have made some study of the chemical nature of soils and plant nutrition.

In what I have termed 'selective feeding and breeding', various species of earthworms were used, habits observed, undesirable members culled out, and gradually cultures of earthworms were obtained which answered the purposes of intensive propagation under control for horticultural, agricultural, and other uses. When I speak of 'domesticated earthworms', I am dealing with native earthworms which have been modified by environment and feeding. When earthworm egg-capsules are hatched out in a new environment, that environment becomes the natural one for the newly hatched worms, whereas a worm which has developed in an entirely different environment might not survive if transplanted into a strange soil. It is this fact of the adaptability of the newly hatched worm to the particular soil in which it is hatched which makes it possible to engage in intensive earthworm culture for the production of egg-capsules which, when placed in a new environment, will hatch worms that are adapted to the soil in which they are born.

So great is the modification of various species of native earthworms, under special environmental conditions and feeding, that the layman or untrained observer may conclude that he has produced a new species of earthworm. However, when we submit the 'domesticated earthworm' to a competent zoologist for laboratory identification and classification, we learn that we are still dealing with some species of native earthworm which has been modified by changes in environment and nutritional factors. Thus when we observe marked changes in earthworms, under special breeding and cultural conditions, we should not jump to the conclusion that we have discovered or produced a

F   65

new species of earthworm. As stated before, earthworms have survived through remote geological ages down to the present practically unchanged as to species, but with widely varying characteristics in different localities, such characteristics being due to the fact that the worms change and adapt themselves to the nutritional environment into which they have been hatched. The wide distribution of earthworms throughout the earth is due to the fact that they can adapt themselves to new environments and new foods.

Regardless of where earthworms are found, or what species we are dealing with, the one important fact to bear in mind is that all of them accomplish the same end—they eat their way through the earth, swallowing the soil with all that it contains, carrying it through the digestive mill of the alimentary canal, and finally ejecting it as highly refined and conditioned topsoil.

At this point, I wish to give full credit to the late Dr. George Sheffield Oliver for the development of the 'domesticated earthworm' which I have used in my soil-building research. In the story of 'My Grandfather's Earthworm Farm', we have the background of Dr. Oliver's later experiments and accomplishments in earthworm culture. His experiences as a small boy on that Ohio farm implanted in his young mind those ineradicable memories and impressions, with definite knowledge of the value of earthworms, which many years later led him into intensive earthworm farming. More than forty years after leaving his grandfather's farm, Dr. Oliver found himself engaged in landscape gardening. His mind naturally turned to ways and means for utilizing his early knowledge of earthworms. Recalling that great earthworm culture bed in his grandfather's barnyard, about which the whole economy of the farm revolved, he began his own experiments with earthworms, which led to the development of the domesticated earthworm. To the day of his death Dr. Oliver was firmly convinced that he had succeeded in producing a hybrid earthworm. This point is not highly important. The important point is that through his work of selective feeding and breeding he did succeed in producing an earthworm with characteristics which answer perfectly all the requirements for intensive propagation and use. To get first-hand information on the development of this modified worm, I applied to Dr. Oliver himself. The story is best given in his own words, a letter written under date of 30th January 1940, which I quote as follows:

DEAR DOCTOR BARRETT,

In answer to your request for information about the development of what you call the domesticated earthworm, it is a long story. It would take a rather large book to record the details of my ups and downs while experimenting with earthworms. I will try to give you the essential facts as briefly as possible. To begin with, your term 'domesticated earthworm' is a quite appropriate name, for the worms which I have developed certainly like to live at home. One of their most valuable characteristics is that they do not wander away from the vicinity where the home colony has been established.

As you know, my interest in earthworms dates from the time I lived for a number of years on my grandfather's farm back in Ohio. Later on, Charles Darwin brought out his famous book on the *Formation of Vegetable Mould Through the Action of Earthworms*, which confirmed in a scientific way what I had already learned from practical experience. From time immemorial farmers and gardeners have recognized that plants and vegetables prosper in soil where there are plenty of earthworms, but few have given any thought to why this is true. In general, people who have worked with the soil have simply accepted earthworms as one of the inhabitants of good soil, never realizing that the worm had anything to do with the building of the soil.

In my investigations I found scattered instances where farmers who fertilized their land with manure from neighbourhood stables attempted to transplant manure-bred worms to their fields. Every attempt ultimately failed, as the transplanted worms did not survive. So far as I have been able to learn, no sincere attempt was made to discover why such earthworms perished when moved. My own experiments and research brought to light the fact that earthworms are as much in need of the food and soil on which they have been raised as fish is in

67

need of water. Manure-bred worms demand manure; soil-bred worms demand soil and decaying vegetable matter and humus. My first efforts to develop a satisfactory hybrid earthworm were made in 1927 when I was engaged in landscape artistry. Selected specimens of earthworms found in various sections of the United States were studied, bred and interbred. Most of my observations, coming under practical conditions, showed that the brandling (commonly known as the manure worm) possessed highly favourable qualities which, if transmitted and retained by a hybrid, would be very advantageous. Chief among these favourable qualities was the fact that the brandling never deposited its excretions above the surface of the soil. One of the main objections which has been made to the use of earthworms (in fact, about the only legitimate objection) is the habit of the ordinary native earthworm of building little piles of lobed castings on lawns and golf links. On lawns such piles of castings are unsightly, while on golf links they are such a nuisance that in many places the worms are killed out by the use of poisons and mineral fertilizers. Golf requires perfectly smooth surfaces for best results and the little hillocks of castings made by the earthworms are often large enough to divert the ball. In some sections, particularly in England, the native earthworms produce such mounds of castings that lawns, golf courses, and cricket grounds have to be rolled regularly in order to keep the surface smooth for good sport and sightliness.

So the quality of delivering its excretions under the surface is a most desirable one; and a most necessary one if earthworms are to be used extensively in choice lawns and golf courses. A second important point in considering the brandling is the fact that, by leaving its castings under the surface of the soil near the root-zone, all the valuable elements of plant food in the castings are readily available to the roots of plants and vegetables; also, the thoroughly humidified castings, with high ammonia content, are not exposed to the air and dried out.

Another characteristic of the manure worm (brandling) is its habit of living close to the surface, seldom going deeper than six inches. Such a burrowing earthworm will cultivate the soil thoroughly about the upper roots of plants and vegetables. I'

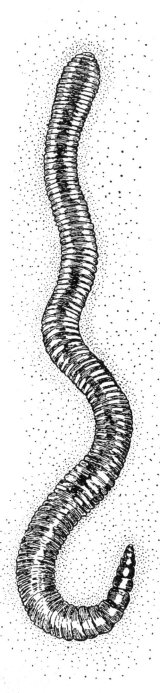

FIG. 2. Native earthworm (*Lumbricus terrestris*). Popular American names—rainworm, night crawler, angleworm, orchard worm. Size, 6 to 12 inches

(*After Hofmeister*)

was my desire to retain this valuable characteristic, if possible, but at the same time secure a worm that would burrow deep into the soil and bring up the subsoil, with its rich chemical elements so necessary in the renewal of the topsoil.

My search for a deep-burrowing earthworm to mate with the brandling was finally rewarded. I examined the earth about the deep roots of large trees which were being transplanted and discovered numerous earthworms which evidently spent most of the time deep in the ground. Such worms have been found as deep as ten to twelve feet or more, and very generally five and six feet deep. This worm was a large species of *Lumbricus terrestris* (orchard worm, rainworm, night lion, angleworm, and a number of other popular names in different localities), of an average length of six to eight inches, but sometimes reaching ten to twelve inches in size, whereas the manure worm is a medium-sized worm of an average length of three or four inches.

Being satisfied that this type of orchard worm would be ideal for experimentation, I selected healthy specimens of both the brandling and the orchard worm in the hope of producing a fertile cross. These were placed in a special mixture of approximately one-third soil, one-third vegetable humus, and one-third decayed animal manure. Such a composition contains all the elements necessary for plant life and in this instance contained plenty of food suitable for both the brandling and the orchard worm.

In the course of time examination of the soil revealed earthworm capsules, and copulation of the earthworms was observed. I carefully gleaned these first capsules from the soil and placed them in a separate container. When these were hatched and grew to near maturity, the weaker and less promising were culled out and the stronger ones were retained as breeders. During the first six months about one thousand hybrids had been selected as breeders and were mating and producing fertile eggs. For a period of several years I continued careful selective breeding and feeding until I had developed a hybrid which breeds true to form and is perfectly adapted for intensive propagation and use in horticulture and agriculture.

While the story of my experiments appears very simple in

the recounting, it should be stated that a full five years were consumed in these experiments. However, the results obtained in orchards, nurseries, gardens, lawns, and poultry houses have proved that this five years' time spent was fully justified. To summarize results for the earthworm culturist, from a practical standpoint, this domesticated hybrid has many characteristics of special value, some of them being:

It is a prolific breeder, under favourable conditions producing one egg capsule every seven days. A very high percentage of the capsules are fertile and they hatch out from four to twenty young worms each.

It is a free animal, readily adapting itself to any food environment or soil. Thus all the wastes of the ordinary family can be composted and used for earthworm food. It turns these end-products into rich humus, practically odourless and containing all the elements necessary for growing choice plants and vegetables.

It is not migratory. Thus when a breeding colony is established under a tree, in a flower-bed, under a rosebush, or elsewhere, the home breeding centre remains and the worms gradually spread in all directions in an ever-widening circle, until all the surrounding ground is thickly populated with this prolific breeder and cultivator of the soil.

A point which should be strongly emphasized is that this hybrid worm produces a very fine, granular casting instead of a lobed casting. The castings do not stick together, but are deposited as a very evenly distributed layer on the surface. In loose, crumbly material, many of the castings are deposited below the surface in proximity to the rootlets where they are needed.

While I was not experimenting particularly to produce fish bait, this hybrid is unexcelled for bait. It is very active, of a good red colour, and will remain alive on a fish-hook for a number of hours when properly impaled.

It is a medium-sized worm, averaging only three to four inches in length when fully mature. This is especially advantageous in the case of delicate flowers and fine seedlings, as the small worm riddles the earth with its fine aerating tunnels without disturbing the tiny rootlets and without drying out the soil too much.

Such, in brief, is the story of the evolution of the 'domesticated earthworm'. I feel that in writing your book on *Harnessing the Earthworm* you are doing a real and lasting service to humanity. I look forward with keen interest and anticipation to its publication.

Cordially yours,
GEORGE SHEFFIELD OLIVER.

DOMESTICATED EARTHWORMS VERSUS NATIVE EARTHWORMS

The question is frequently asked, 'Why go to the expense of purchasing domesticated earthworms, if native earthworms do the same work?' Our answer is that anything worth doing is worth doing well. By taking advantage of the experience of those who have spent years in study and research, the beginner can avoid many mistakes and much expensive labour. Earthworm culture is very much the same as working with other animals or with plants. The labour is the main cost put into the work. It takes just as much time to work with scrub stock as with thoroughbreds. It takes the same amount of time to grow a seedling tree as to grow some choice variety that has been developed and tested.

While earthworm culture can be established and developed with the available native worms, it pays to make the start with the domesticated variety, as they are sure to be prolific, are adaptable to all sorts of food and soil, and will work the year round where the temperature is warm enough. The small expense of starting right is soon absorbed in the results obtained. One friend wrote us that he started with 250 earthworm egg-capsules and within two years he estimated that he had 500,000 breeders in his culture bed. Once adequate breeding stock has been developed, earthworm production can be carried into astronomical figures very quickly by composting and handling the material properly. The life of one man is too short to carry out original research into the subject. But this is not necessary,

72

FIG. 3. Domesticated earthworm. Average life-size of mature worm is 4 inches long

as the facts have already been established through long years of experimentation by many different people. Darwin's experiments and research extended over a period of more than fifty years before he published his findings. Since the time of Darwin, literally thousands of experimenters, including scientists, laymen, and practical farmers and gardeners, have verified the facts which he established. Therefore, it is not necessary to carry out long experimentation for verification of the basic facts.

Our advice to those who desire to make a start in earthworm culture is: *Secure an adequate supply of domesticated earthworm egg-capsules, or a culture of domesticated earthworms, and go to work.* The technique of intensive propagation and use is so simple that a child can understand and follow it. Materials used in breeding earthworms are the same materials that should be incorporated into the soil anyway in building up and maintaining a high state of productive fertility. By utilizing these materials through earthworm culture, results are much more quickly obtained and more satisfactory than by the ordinary methods. After all, the main expense in soil-building is the time and labour spent. Once earthworm culture is established, the small initial investment of money in making the right start is soon absorbed in increased land values, increased production, and increased living satisfaction.

IX

BREEDING HABITS OF THE EARTHWORM

Each individual of the earthworm family is both male and female (hermaphrodite), having both eggs and spermatozoa, but it is not self-fertilizing. An act of copulation is necessary in order that the eggs may become fertile. Situated behind the head about one-third the length of the worm is the 'clitellum', a band of tissue surrounding the body. The Century Dictionary gives a very good definition of the clitellum. We quote in part: '. . . the saddle of an annelid, as the earthworm; a peculiar glandular ring around the body, resulting from the swelling and other modification of certain segments. It is a sexual organ, producing a tough, viscid secretion by which two worms are bound together in a kind of copulation.' The clitellum is easily identified, as it stands out above the surface of the body as a distinct band, darker in colour than the rest of the body.

In a bulletin entitled, *The Earthworms of Ohio*, issued by the Ohio Biological Survey, Dr. Henry W. Olson gives a very concise and clear description of the act of copulation and the reproductive functions of earthworms. We quote in part from this description:

'Each individual is a male and female (hermaphrodite), so any one of the same species will do for a mate. Though having both eggs and spermatozoa, they are not self-fertilizing, but mutually fertilize each other's eggs. . . .

'The two worms meet and overlap one another to about one-third to one-fourth of their lengths, with the heads facing in opposite directions and the ventral sides in contact. They then secrete quantities of viscous mucus, which forms a thick band about the clitellar regions of their bodies. These mucous bands surround both bodies and serve to bind the copulating individuals tightly together. Each worm then acts as a male, giving off a quantity of seminal fluid that is conducted along the

75

grooves to the seminal receptacles of the other, where it is picked up and stored. After the worms have separated, the slime tube which is formed by the clitellum of the worm is worked forward over the body, collecting albumen from the glands of the ventral side. As it passes over the fourteenth segment, it collects a few eggs from the oviducts and then passes the ninth and tenth segments, where it receives spermatozoa from the seminal receptacles where they have been stored up. The sperm then fertilizes the eggs. The slime tube is gradually slipped off over the head, closing up as though with a draw-string, as first its anterior end and then its posterior end slips off over the sharp prostomium.

'This closed slime tube, with the fertilized eggs and nutritive fluid which it contains, constitutes the cocoon. In this cocoon the eggs develop directly into the young worms, which, when ready to emerge, crawl out through one end of the cocoon after the slime plug has been dissolved away. The cocoons vary in size and shape, according to the species. The smallest are hardly one millimetre in length, while the largest are as large as eight millimetres. . . . In *Lumbricus terrestris* (commonly known as the orchard worm, rainworm, and various other popular names), the capsules are lemon-shaped, having an olive colour. The number of eggs in the capsules of *Helodrilus trapezoides* is from three to eight; in those of *Lumbricus terrestris* it is from four to twenty. All of the eggs of the *Lumbricus terrestris* become fecundated and develop; on the other hand, in the capsules of *H. trapezoides* one egg only, or rarely two or three, produce embryos. . . . The embryos escape as small worms in about two to three weeks.'

Under favourable conditions, which means plenty of food, moisture, and mild summer temperature, the domesticated earthworm will produce one of the lemon-shaped egg-capsules every seven to ten days. The capsule (cocoon) may contain from two or three to as high as twenty fertile eggs. In a moist, warm environment, the incubating period is from two to three weeks.

The newborn worms first appear as whitish bits of thread, about one-quarter inch long or smaller. They gradually become darker within a few hours and within a few days can be readily identified as tiny, reddish-coloured earthworms. To the untrained eye, the newborn worms are visible only after a careful search for them. Except for size, they are hatched as full-fledged earthworms and immediately begin their life-work of devouring earth with all it contains, digesting and utilizing the organic food

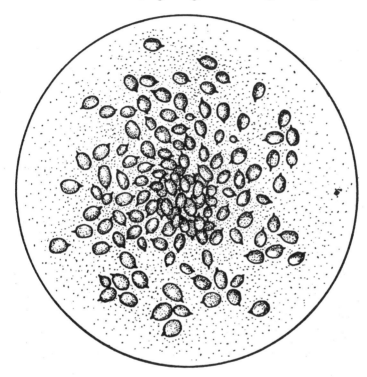

FIG. 4. Domesticated earthworm eggs, called 'egg-capsules' (*Pen drawing—natural size*)

material from the ingested earth, and finally depositing the residue on or near the surface as castings.

While the newborn worms are hard to see, there is no difficulty in identifying the egg-capsules. The colour is usually radically different from that of the soil, varying from light lemon colour in freshly passed capsules to a dark purple in capsules nearing maturity and ready to hatch. Size varies, depending on the size of the worm from which they come, ranging from the

77 .

size of a pin-head to about the size of a grain of rice. A handful of earth from a properly prepared culture box may contain several dozen capsules.

While the normal incubating period at right temperature has been stated to be from two to three weeks, this period may be extended almost indefinitely by drying out the capsules or by refrigeration. Under ordinary conditions of temperature and moisture as found in the earth at the time the capsules are produced, they will incubate and hatch within the normal period. On the other hand, if the capsules happen to be subjected to the heat of the sun and dry out, or are dried purposely for preservation, they may remain dormant and fertile for months and then swell and develop under proper temperature and moisture. Capsules have been reported to have hatched out after lying dormant for eighteen months. Also, capsules may be placed in refrigeration at temperatures ranging from fifty degrees and lower, and thus kept dormant and fertile until they are desired for use. In frozen ground and manure piles and frozen compost heaps, as soon as the spring thaw comes and the earth or manure warms up, great numbers of capsules which have been dormant will hatch out. This stability of the fertile eggs under many different conditions accounts for the very wide distribution of the earthworm over the earth, from the far north to the tropics, from sea level to high altitudes. Capsules become dried out and are carried great distances and scattered by the wind in new locations. They may stick to dry soil on the hoofs or hides of animals and be transported from one place to another. They are sometimes swallowed by birds and fail to digest and are then dropped in a new location, perhaps on a high mountain or on an island of the sea, or some other out-of-the-way place where it would have been impossible for a mature worm to find its way. Earthworm capsules are often transported great distances on the roots of plants and start a colony hundreds or thousands of miles from the original location. On account of this stability, it is possible to produce earthworm egg-capsules commercially and ship them to any part of the world, thus enabling people anywhere to establish intensive earthworm culture for impregnation of the earth or for other purposes.

BREEDING HABITS OF THE EARTHWORM

After hatching, the young worm develops rapidly and in from sixty to ninety days will reach the reproductive stage and may begin to produce capsules. This does not mean that the worm is fully grown in this length of time, but means that the reproductive organs have reached a point of maturity where they will begin to function. The egg-capsules from these young worms may be almost microscopic in size and difficult to find. It will usually require several months to a year for a domesticated earthworm to reach full mature size, averaging about four inches in length. If desired for use as fish-bait, the older worms are best.

In a favourable environment an earthworm will live for many years. One report was given of an observation carried out for a period of fifteen years and the worm under this experiment appeared just as young as ever. As a matter of fact, the earthworm is about as nearly perfect a digestive apparatus as can be conceived in the animal world. Its secretions take care of every form of food, both acid and alkaline—sugars, starches, proteins, fats. Equipped with a powerful gizzard, it does not have to select or chew the food. The worm swallows anything small enough to enter its mouth, including grains of sand and small stones which act as millstones in the gizzard, which grinds and mixes everything. It absorbs and assimilates nutrients from the swallowed material. It breathes through the skin and eliminates through the skin. So, barring accidental destruction, earthworms should enjoy comparative immortality in the flesh, remaining eternally youthful through perfect assimilation and elimination.

As earthworms are both male and female in one body, a colony may be established from one fertile earthworm or from a single egg-capsule. With a capsule being produced every seven to ten days and hatching from one or two to twenty worms, it can be seen that production will soon reach astronomical figures. Those who are particularly interested in mathematics can take a pencil and paper and figure it out. There is no difficulty or problem in the production of plenty of worms, even into the millions, once the simple technique is studied and a start made.

X

EARTHWORM CULTURE

Intensive propagation for maximum results in soil-building requires large numbers of worms, depending on the amount of land to be used for garden, orchard, or farm. It should be borne in mind and emphasized that intensive use of earthworms bears about the same relation to earthworms as found in nature as a power installation for production of electricity, such as Niagara Falls, Boulder Dam, or Bonneyville Dam, has to the unharnessed water power flowing down a native stream. We use from one thousand to five thousand times the concentrations of breeding earthworms per cubic foot of composted material as would be found in the average natural environment with the native earthworm population.

The small city gardener may have only a few square feet of earth, or possibly just a few potted plants or a window-box. Others may have a small kitchen vegetable garden or flower garden. Still others may have a market garden or nursery, and so on up to extensive acreage in orchard, farm, or ranch. Earthworm culture may be engaged in successfully, whether it be for producing fine potting material for a few plants, a small garden, or for acreage of any extent. A start may be made in a one-gallon can or a small box, beginning with a few earthworm eggs (called egg-capsules), or a few worms. The technique is practically the same, regardless of the size of the background.

In a few words, the way to begin earthworm culture is to provide a culture medium of earthworm food in some kind of container or bed—a tin can, a small wooden box, a compost heap, or a specially designed culture bed—add a few egg-capsules or worms, and keep the culture thoroughly moist and shaded. Further discussion of earthworm food will come later. We have already covered the subject of food for worms in a general manner. Results obtained will, of course, be commensurate with the care and effort expended. Engaging in earthworm culture is very much like starting in to raise chickens. One can start with a few eggs and increase slowly, or start with a large number of eggs and increase rapidly. For a small yard or garden, a small setting is all that is required—one or two cans or box cultures. For a greater amount of land, a proportionately greater beginning should be made. As an example of the rapidity of increase which can be made from a small beginning, one thousand egg-capsules were incubated and hatched out. From this start four lug box cultures (see illustrations and instructions on box culture) of five hundred worms each were set up. Within one year from the time this set-up was made, a total of 55,000 egg-capsules had been harvested from these four boxes. The increase was used to impregnate extensive soil-building culture beds and compost heaps and at the end of the first year vast numbers of the soil-builders were at work and multiplying in many tons of composted soil-building material.

Once the initial beginning is made, with a modest cash investment of from perhaps £1 to about £5, the main money-cost involved is the small amount of labour required in taking care of the cultures. The material which is used in providing soil-building food for the worms is the same material which should be incorporated into the soil anyway in building and maintaining the highest state of fertility.

Where too small a beginning is made, one is apt to become discouraged with the slow progress made in building up an adequate number of breeding earthworms to show satisfactory results. Therefore we advise the beginner in earthworm culture to make a sizable start. It requires about as much time to look after a single culture box or bed as it does to take care of a number of boxes. Once the start is made, the main attention for sixty to ninety days will be to sprinkle the cultures with water about once a week, or often enough to keep them moist while the worms are developing.

In giving instructions for making a beginning and proceeding with perfect confidence in success, we shall not discuss makeshift methods. More labour, the main consideration, is involved

G   81

in following makeshift methods than will be found necessary in doing the thing right. Let us, therefore, proceed on the principle that 'anything worth doing is worth doing well'. I wish to emphasize that the methods herein described are not arbitrary, except for certain basic principles. In my research and experimentation over a period of a good many years, I have invented or evolved methods, culture beds, and so on, which have proved successful in my own work, as well as in the work of many others who have taken up earthworm culture and followed the methods I have advised. I further counsel every earthworm culturist to experiment constantly and work out methods of his own. In this way comes progress.

INTENSIVE EARTHWORM CULTURE IN BOXES

Vegetable Lug Boxes

The simplest and most practical method for beginning earthworm culture is propagation in boxes. Many years' experience in the intensive breeding of earthworms for egg-capsule production have demonstrated that a box of the approximate dimensions of 14 inches wide, 18 inches long, and 6 inches deep is the best size both for convenient and easy handling and maximum capsule production, in order to develop quickly and maintain a steady supply of earthworm eggs for production of breeding stock and for impregnating extensive culture beds and compost heaps, as well as flower pots, beds, lawns, trees, shrubs, and soil in general.

I have found that the standard vegetable lug box, which has an overall measurement of 14 inches wide, 17½ inches long and 6 inches deep, answers all purposes for setting up earthworm culture. Such boxes are usually obtainable at the grocery or market at a very reasonable cost. Lug boxes are light in weight, quite strong and durable, and serve the purpose admirably.

To conserve space, boxes may be stacked in tiers four to ten boxes high. Tiers four or five boxes high are most convenient for easy handling. The tiers should be supported above floor or ground upon a base about six inches high. Such a base support may be made from 2 inches by 6 inches timber, stood on

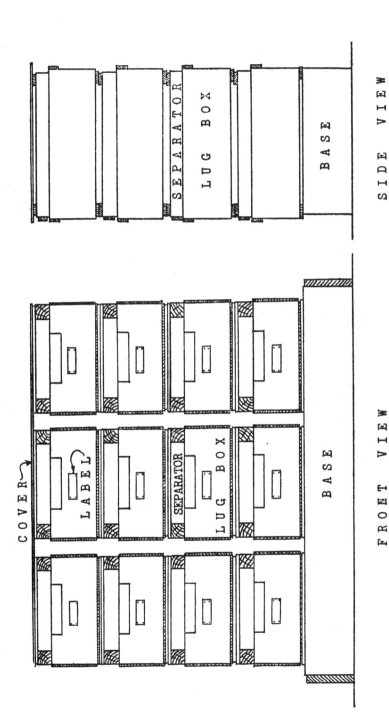

Fig. 5. Lug boxes: front and side view

edge and properly spaced apart by cleats firmly nailed across the ends. Fig. 7 shows the details of a base support with overall dimensions 46 inches long and 17¼ inches wide, designed to support three tiers of boxes. Such a base may be made any length desired, but we have found in practice that in levelling the base it is much easier to adjust a short base in a perfectly level position, especially on uneven ground, than it is to adjust a long base. Also, in shifting a base from one location to another, the short, light base is more convenient to handle.

The purpose of the base support is to provide ventilation and drainage and also to prevent escape of the breeder worms. Breeding boxes set flat upon the ground or floor provide a cool, damp spot underneath the box and the worms may congregate or escape under the box and burrow into the ground. Supported on a base above floor or ground, the worms will remain in the boxes where the food and moisture are.

By the use of separators between the boxes (see Figs. 6 and 7), made of 2 inches by 2 inches material, 17½ inches long and spaced 13¼ inches apart by lath cleats, the watering of cultures is facilitated. A hose nozzle or flat sprinkler-head can be inserted between the boxes without disturbing the tiers and the entire tier can thus be watered in one or two minutes. Once the cultures are set up, all the attention they require between harvest times—three or four weeks apart—is watering once or twice a week, depending on the weather and temperature. In hot, dry weather more watering is required than in cool, wet weather. Cultures should be kept thoroughly moist at all times for best results. In watering, a gentle sprinkler stream should be used so that the surface of the culture will not be rudely disturbed by the force of a hard stream or spray. I always use a layer of gunny sack material on top of the culture material in each box. The gunny sacking conserves moisture and prevents drying out; and also acts as a water spreader, ensuring even spread of the water and preventing disturbance of the culture material by force of the water.

EARTHWORM CULTURE

Gunny Sacks

I have found that plenty of gunny sacks are almost indispensable in earthworm culture. Old potato sacks, sugar sacks, meal sacks—in fact, old sacks of any kind—provide material for a multitude of purposes. I use them for cover material to protect the cultures from excessive heat and cold, for shade in the form of screens tacked on a lath or other light framework. Their main use, however, is as cover material on the surface of the compost in all boxes and culture beds. Such cover material conserves moisture, keeps the surface of the culture dark and damp, and favours maximum capsule-production. The worms will congregate in great numbers immediately below the damp layer of burlap and this encourages rapid breeding. I use a heavy pair of tin snips for cutting the sacks into convenient sizes. Ordinary scissors may be used, but they are not heavy enough for regular use. With tin snips, one can cut several layers of sacking at a time, thus speeding up the process. I have also discovered that it is much easier to cut wet sacks than dry ones. So I usually soak a number of sacks in a tub of water and cut them to the proper dimensions for future use, according to the size of the culture beds to be covered. In large culture beds, I do not cut the sacks at all. For lug box cultures one sack will provide for four boxes, the edges of the squares being folded over at the sides and ends of boxes.

Preparation of Boxes

Properly prepared culture boxes will last from two to four years. Therefore an expenditure of time, plus a few pennies' cost in material, is fully justified. Also we have found that there is much greater satisfaction to be derived from things well done than from careless work. Boxes of the proper dimensions may be made, the size not being fixed so long as the depth is kept at about six inches. In intensive propagation for capsule production the depth is important. Earthworms breed at the surface for the most part; so in shallow box cultures they quickly congregate on the surface under the damp burlap cover.

If vegetable lug boxes are used, select good boxes without

large knot holes. For drainage bore six to eight quarter-inch holes, properly spaced over the bottom of the box. The cracks in the bottom provide additional drainage. Reinforce the bottom of the box by nailing a lath cleat across it at each end, thus preventing the thin boards from splitting off around the nailheads. For each box, cut ten pieces of plasterer's lath, thirteen inches long, to be placed crosswise in the bottom of the box. This distributes the weight of the wet compost evenly over the bottom of the box, provides drainage, and prevents sagging of the bottom boards. Also when the contents of the box are dumped, the crosswise lath prevents the wet compost from adhering to the bottom. The lath may be used over and over again, like the box. For convenient handling, a small strip of lath, six inches long, should be tacked on each end of the box, near the upper edge, so that the box can be firmly grasped in lifting. In Figs. 5, 6, and 7 and Plate IV are a photograph of a lug box unit, and line-drawings to show the details described above. I suggest very careful study and attention to details.

Compost Mixing

We usually speak of earthworm food as 'compost'. While the compost may be thoroughly mixed in any convenient way, on a bare spot of ground, in a box or other container, I have found a mixing box, similar to a cement-mixing trough, a very convenient and practical thing to have on hand. Such a mixing box should be about twelve inches deep, three feet wide, and five to six feet long, with smooth wood or metal bottom and sloping ends. A metal bottom, supported by wood, is preferred, as this makes a practically waterproof box and there is no waste of water while mixing compost. Three cubic feet of material can be conveniently mixed in such a box. Any surplus material not used can be stored in the box and kept moist for future use. The rotting of the material thus stored increases its value as earthworm food. The compost can be mixed with a rake, hoe, or shovel, in the same manner that cement is mixed. It is well to screen the earth first in order to remove small stones or hard clods, using a half-inch mesh screen, or even as fine a screen as quarter-inch mesh. The sloping ends of the mixing box facilitate the mixing and emptying of the box. Compost for lug boxes should be very thoroughly broken up by chopping, raking, or screening, similar to the preparation of fine potting material. The finer the result, the better. It should be borne in mind that earthworms have no teeth and that they can swallow particles no larger than the mouth opening.

While the preliminary mixing should be made with practically dry material, it can be lightly sprinkled to lay the flying dust. As the material becomes well broken up, it should be sprinkled more and more, so that when it is ready for use it will be a crumbly mass, damp through and through, but not muddy or 'soggy'. Compost should not be 'flooded', as this tends to 'puddle' the fine soil and make a dense mass instead of a crumbly, loamy compost. A good plan is to mix a tray of compost as outlined and then sprinkle it daily for two or three days, turning it thoroughly at each sprinkling. In this way the material will absorb the water evenly through and through. With lug box propagation no time or trouble should be begrudged in the preparation of material for capsule production.

Lug Box Compost Material

For lug box culture, a fine compost may be prepared of one part manure, one part screened topsoil, and one part agricultural peat moss. A mixture of manures may be used. However, we prefer a mixture of horse and rabbit manure, half-and-half, finely broken up, or a mixture made from rabbit manure only. In considering the kind of manure to use, the available source of manure must be taken into account. For large compost beds, where from a cubic yard to several tons of material is composted, all kinds of manures and vegetable waste, including garbage, can be used to advantage; but for intensive production of capsules in lug boxes, it is highly desirable to have a very fine compost of crumbly material that is not too disagreeable or messy to handle with the bare hands or with gloves. In addition to the material as outlined, I usually work into the compost a liberal sprinkling of some standard, all-purpose chicken mash or corn meal. Corn meal has been found to favour the formation of egg-capsules. If mash is used, the proportion should be about one-half to one pound for each cubic foot of finished compost. If corn meal is used, about one-half pound for each cubic foot of finished compost is sufficient. The mash or corn meal ensures a ration of carbohydrates, proteins, and fats for the worms, so that they will be well-nourished, regardless of the organic composition of the composted soil-building material. Maximum production in box culture is dependent on plenty of food. The mash or corn meal should be added before the compost has been wet, so that it can be uniformly distributed throughout the mixture.

Measuring and Quality of Materials

In preparing compost for box culture, we usually mix about three cubic feet of material, which is about all the mixing box will accommodate. An apple box is a handy measure, as it holds approximately a cubic foot. It is not necessary to bother with too fine a measure, as the proportions as outlined are approximate only. So we take an apple box, or other measure, of manure; one box of good loamy topsoil, and one box of agricultural peat moss, plus three pounds of chicken mash, or one and a half pounds of corn meal. The peat may be soaked previously, broken up, and squeezed out. It requires several hours' time fully to impregnate peat with water. I usually soak it twenty-four hours before mixing the compost and then squeeze the surplus water out. Materials should be measured dry, as they bulk up after water is added. Peat moss is best for lug box culture, as the idea is to provide a compost that will retain a high water content without being soggy or muddy. For large compost beds, straw, hay, leaves, or other vegetable matter may be substituted for peat. Lug box culture is used particularly for production of large numbers of egg-capsules for impregnation of more extensive compost beds and soil areas. Therefore greater care may be taken and a small additional expense incurred. Commercially, egg-capsules are valued at about a half-penny each, the value being based on labour cost for production and handling. We value a lug box culture of five hundred breeder worms at something like £3. However, in production for use in impregnating soil, millions of capsules can be propa-

PLATE V. The Earthmaster Culture Bed, construction details

PLATE VI. The Earthmaster Culture Bed, construction details

(a)

(b)

PLATE VII. (a) Christopher Gallup; (b) his chief tool, the spring-tooth
harrow and tractor with which he feeds his earthworms

gated at practically no cost other than the cost of the cheap and abundant material used for earthworm food. The parent materials of topsoil used in earthworm culture are, as I have already pointed out, the identical materials which should be added to the soil anyway to rebuild and maintain fertile and productive land. The utilization of earthworms in transforming the culture material is the most rapid and efficient method, and also produces better soil than any other means.

Loading Culture Boxes with Earthworms

A layer of alfalfa hay about one inch deep should be placed in the bottom of the culture box; or two or three thicknesses of old potato sack material (or other gunny sacking) can be used instead of the hay. The hay or burlap improves drainage, prevents compost from adhering to the bottom of the box, and is liked by the earthworms as food. Then fill the box about two-thirds full of the prepared compost. Five hundred breeder earthworms should be placed on top of the compost. If the worms have been received in a shipping container, they will be mixed with prepared earthworm food. The entire contents of the container can be dumped into the prepared box, raked lightly over the surface of the compost, and may be covered with a few additional handfuls of compost. While the compost should not be packed, it is well to smooth and 'firm' the surface before adding the worms. A handy tool for this purpose is a plasterer's metal trowel, or a cement finisher's wooden float. A triangular block of wood will answer the purpose. The worms will quickly work down into the compost, making their own burrows. After the worms are added, cover the surface with one or two thicknesses of burlap, which should be well soaked before using. I have already discussed the uses of burlap. I usually cut an old gunny sack into four to eight pieces, approximately the size of the top of the box. If the sacking is larger than the box, the edges may be folded over inside the box. This burlap cover does not need to be disturbed until the culture is ready for servicing. The cultures are sprinkled from time to time through this covering, which acts as a spreader for the water and prevents the water from disturbing the surface of the culture. As the burlap rots and disintegrates, it becomes food for the worms and a fresh cover is added as necessary. Experience has proved that such a cover conserves the moisture and prevents the surface from drying out, provides a dark surface, and fosters capsule production.

Impregnating Culture Boxes with Egg-Capsules

The culture boxes for capsules are prepared the same as for breeder worms, as described in the preceding paragraph. Spread two or three hundred earthworm egg-capsules over the surface of the compost and cover with one inch of additional compost. Cover with damp burlap, exactly as outlined for breeder worms. Place in a warm place for incubating and hatching. A temperature of from fifty to seventy degrees in the shade is warm enough. A shed, basement, or other shady place can be utilized. At the proper temperature, the eggs will incubate and hatch in from fourteen to twenty-one days. The newly spawned worms will develop quite rapidly in a warm environment and will reach the reproductive stage in from sixty to ninety days. The culture should not be disturbed during development, except for the necessary watering. Contents of the culture box should be kept moist at all times. After sixty days, the culture may be examined to determine if capsules are being produced. After capsule production is started, the cultures are handled in the same way as the culture boxes of mature worms. A lug box of compost as described has sufficient food to develop one to two thousand worms from capsule to reproductive stage. Thus, a thousand or more egg-capsules may be used in a single box, incubated and hatched out and developed over a period of from sixty to ninety days. Then the culture can be divided into two or more boxes. Through experience I have found that about five hundred mature worms to a lug box give the best results in capsule production. If there are too many breeders, they may slow down in reproduction. Although earthworms begin to produce capsules while they are quite small, the fully mature worms will be the best breeders as a rule. Worms live to a great age, unless accidentally destroyed, provided they are in a favourable environment.

EARTHWORM CULTURE

Watering Culture Boxes

If worms are to multiply rapidly, they must have plenty of water. The compost should be kept moist through and through, but not soggy. The boxes should be watered with a sprinkler hose, sprinkling can, or hose nozzle once or twice a week, according to what is necessary to keep the cultures moist. Proper state of moisture must be determined by inspection until experience shows correct routine and time for watering. The point of prime importance is never to allow the cultures to 'dry out'. Preliminary to harvesting the increase, the culture boxes may be allowed to become somewhat dry for a few days, so that the material can be handled without trouble. Wet, muddy compost is not so easily handled as is a moist, crumbly material. Many small details of production and handling will be learned by experience—in fact, that is the only way that they can be learned.

Harvesting the Increase—Proper Work Tables

A table of twenty-eight inches high, thirty inches wide, of any desired length, is a convenient size for harvesting operations. It is well to have a railing on the back and ends of the table, about three inches high, to prevent the material from being pushed off the table. The table-top should be smooth, preferably covered with metal, and without cracks. Dump contents of a culture box on the table and rake the material into a cone-shaped pile. The material which adheres to the sides and bottom of the box can be carefully scraped out with a small trowel, old case-knife, putty knife, or spatula. Never use a sharp cutting tool in handling earthworms. While they will stand considerable handling, they should not be cut or injured. If there are a number of boxes to be serviced, a long table can be used and several boxes dumped at one time. During the harvesting, the work-table should be in a lighted place, either mild sunshine or under electric light. Worms are very sensitive to light and will quickly burrow down toward the bottom and centre of the compost in trying to escape from it. Have the same number of culture boxes prepared as have been dumped. The old boxes which have been dumped should be prepared again, the same as the original culture boxes. The old boxes will have the original labels on them and can be used for the breeder worms over and over again.

After waiting a few minutes after dumping, to allow the worms to work down away from the surface, start the harvesting operation by raking the material from the surface of the cone-shaped pile. Proceed lightly, with the fingers, so as not to injure the worms. An inch or more of material can usually be removed at first; the material removed contains the egg-capsules and is placed in the new culture box; wait a few minutes, to allow the worms to work deeper, then repeat the operation; and so on, until two-thirds or more of the old culture material has been transferred to the new box. Any worms encountered should be transferred back to the old culture box. Experience will soon teach how to harvest the increase as rapidly as possible. In following this routine, the breeder worms will be found in the one-third of the old compost remaining on the table. Most of the egg-capsules will have been transferred to the new culture boxes. The harvested material will contain the capsules which have been produced during the two or three weeks preceding the harvest. Also it will contain a good many young worms. I sometimes wait a day or more, after dumping the culture boxes on the work table, before beginning the harvesting. By waiting a considerable length of time, we shall find that most of the worms will have worked down to the bottom of the pile, and we shall thus be able quickly to transfer the top two-thirds or more to the new culture boxes without encountering any worms and without further waiting.

The remainder of the old compost, with the breeder worms, should now be returned to the old culture boxes, the boxes filled with the new compost and prepared as at the original start. The newly loaded boxes with capsules should be properly marked and a new tier of boxes started. These new cultures will require from sixty to ninety days before they are ready for harvesting operations.

With mature, breeding earthworms, harvesting is carried out every twenty-one to thirty days. Incubation period of capsules is fourteen to twenty-one days, depending on moisture, temperature, and other conditions. Therefore, if harvesting is carried out every twenty-one to thirty days, practically all the increase in capsules will be transferred to new culture boxes, to build up additional breeding stock.

Marking Boxes

Any system of marking can be followed by the individual as may suit his own inclination. I usually number and date the boxes, maintaining two series of numbers. One series of numbers is for the mature breeder-earthworms. The other series is for the cultures which are developing from egg-capsules. As the new cultures reach the reproductive age, they are transferred to the breeder series. In setting up new breeder boxes it is well actually to count the worms, allowing five hundred to six hundred per box. It is impossible to recover all the egg-capsules at harvest time and this residue of capsules will hatch out and develop with the mature breeders. In time, the culture boxes will become over-populated. For this reason, the breeder boxes should be worked over from time to time, and the number of worms reduced to from five hundred to six hundred per box. As previously stated, if a culture box becomes too crowded, the worms will cease to produce capsules. They tend to limit their population to correspond to the available food present. I have found that I secure the maximum number of capsules from boxes of between five hundred and six hundred worms each. On the other hand, while the capsules are hatching out and developing, it is all right to have from one thousand to two thousand worms to the box. As they reach the reproductive stage, they can be separated and breeding cultures of the correct number set up. In marking boxes, I have found it convenient to tack a small square of white cardboard to the end of the box, leaving the head of the drawing pin not quite down. Numbers can be typed on the card before attaching to the box, or can be marked with lead pencil or waterproof pencil after they are tacked on. New cards can be provided as the old cards become ragged. By leaving the head of the drawing pin slightly protruding, we can readily take it out for attaching new cards from time to time.

THE EARTHWORM UNDER CONTROL

Building Large Compost Beds

Once an adequate number of lug box cultures of mature breeders have been established, all harvested material can be used for impregnating large compost beds for soil-building and for rapid propagation of vast numbers of earthworms. Or the increase can be used directly for impregnating potted plants, flower-beds, lawns, gardens, shrubs, trees, or orchards. For instance, in orcharding, a group of a hundred lug boxes of five hundred breeders each, properly handled, would produce enough increase to impregnate from one hundred to three hundred trees per month. In impregnating orchards, or other trees or shrubs, the harvested, capsule-bearing material is buried around the trees, well back from the bole, with a cover of prepared compost as a mulch, to conserve moisture and furnish an abundance of available food for the developing worms. Once earthworms are established in the soil, they will take care of themselves. Wherever there is sufficient moisture to maintain good vegetation, the earthworms can survive.

Rapidity of Increase

Under good conditions, which means abundant food and moisture, with temperatures ranging from fifty to seventy or eighty degrees in the shade, earthworms increase with almost incredible rapidity. Mature worms will produce an egg-capsule every seven to ten days. The capsules will incubate and hatch in fourteen to twenty-one days, each egg-capsule producing from one to as many as twenty tiny worms. The newly hatched worms develop rapidly and in sixty to ninety days will begin to produce capsules. I give here a brief summary of two reports received, which will indicate what can be accomplished from a small beginning. In my own experiments I have verified these results many times.

Report No. 1: From San Bernardino, California. An earthworm culturist wrote that he started a lug box culture on 23rd July 1939, with one hundred earthworm egg-capsules. The pertinent part of this man's letter follows: 'On September 24th, just two months after I first "planted" the capsules, I dumped the contents of the lug on the sorting table. After carefully sorting over approximately two-thirds of the lug's contents, I had harvested eight hundred egg-capsules and approximately three hundred earthworms. I obtained another lug box, prepared new compost of the same composition as previously described, and divided my crop into the two lugs. The approximate one-third balance of the unsorted original compost was buried under some ferns in front of my house. Judging from the number of egg-capsules I recovered, eight hundred by actual count, from approximately two-thirds of the original compost, I believe it is conservative to estimate that there were at least one thousand egg-capsules in the entire contents of the original lug. It is my plan to take another census of these two lugs on November 24th, and following that count, I will inform you of my findings. . . . ROY S. M.'

Report No. 2: From Kansas City, Missouri. From a long letter, giving many details of his work in earthworm culture, this Missouri man concludes with this summary: 'I closed my year October 1st. From June 4th, 1943, starting with 1,000 capsules, till September 30th, 1944, I have produced 55,000 capsules. . . . H.A.H.' This man has used his increase in establishing extensive soil-building compost beds and states that he now has vast quantities of the soil-builders at work in these beds multiplying into almost astronomical numbers, while at the same time breaking down the material into highly fertile topdressing for his garden acreage.

I have on file many reports similar to the above, fully verifying my own findings over a period of several years' experimental research in practical earthworm culture and soil-building.

Shade, Temperature, Darkness, Moisture

For intensive capsule production in box cultures, temperatures ranging from sixty to eighty degrees will be found most suitable. Drying out quickly affects worms and will inhibit or stop reproduction. Boxes should be kept fairly dark, as earthworms work in darkness. I usually provide covers for the tiers of boxes, made of old gunny sacks, or other cheap material. Worms prefer to work near the surface. Therefore I

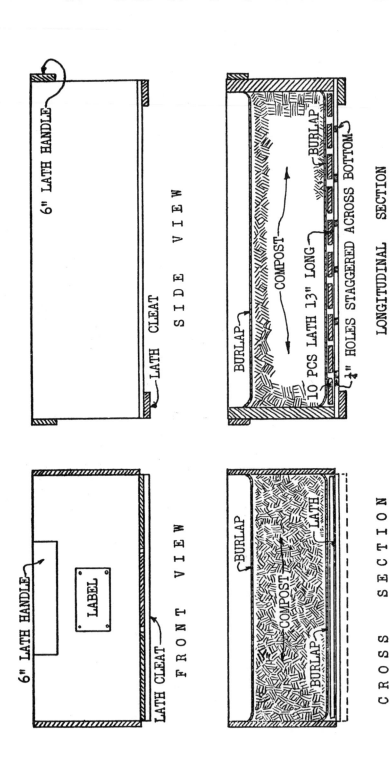

Fig. 6. Detail plan for lug box earthworm culture. Boxes are stacked in tiers on base support

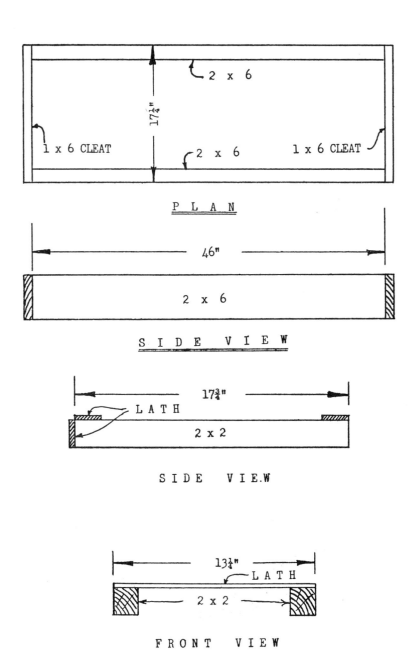

FIG. 7. Plan of base support for lug box stack
Plan of dividers for lug box earthworm culture

H

keep the surface of the culture covered with damp burlap as previously outlined, to conserve moisture and provide darkness on surface of compost. Worms were originally water animals. For intensive production, they still require plenty of water. Cultures should always be moist through and through, though not soggy. This point cannot be too strongly emphasized. Boxes should not be flooded. Good drainage should be maintained in the bottom of the box, so that surplus water will quickly drain out. If cultures are maintained in outdoor shade, the tiers should be protected from flooding rains. Sheds, outhouses, basements, lath-houses, tree shade or other shade will prove satisfactory for earthworm culture fixtures.

Stacking Box Cultures

Culture boxes should not be placed flat on the ground or other surface, for in such cases the worms will gradually work out into the ground or gather under the damp bottom. Therefore, as previously outlined, a support for the tiers of boxes should be made of 2 inches by 6 inches (two pieces) material, stood on edge 13¾ inches apart, with cleats across ends to hold them firmly. Any length base support can be provided, according to the number of tiers that are to be placed on the base. I like a base support to accommodate three tiers, as this size support is easily handled. The tiers are thus supported six inches above the ground. (For details of construction, see Plate IV and Figs. 5 to 7.)

Earthworm Breeding Boxes

I have given detailed drawings for box culture, with descriptive instructions elsewhere. Plate IV shows an actual photograph of two tiers of lug boxes resting on the base. Points to note particularly are: separators between boxes, to allow insertion of hose sprinkler-head for watering; burlap sacks resting between boxes on top of separators, for shade and conservation of moisture; structure of separator; small lath hand-hold on the ends of the boxes; lath strips for placing crosswise in the bottom of the boxes; structure of base support for the tiers. A convenient size base will support three tiers. Tiers may be any height, four to six boxes being best for handling. While the illustration shows tiers without cover, in actual use I cover the stacks with burlap sacks to keep cultures dark and to conserve moisture.

In a unit of this kind I use approximately 500 breeders to the box. I often harvest upwards of 2,000 egg-capsules per month from each box. I use the increase for impregnating large compost breeding beds, flower-beds. lawns, or other land. From this it will be seen that a group of from five to ten culture boxes will quickly develop vast numbers of worms.

Soil-Building Culture Beds

In my methods for developing earthworm culture, I use lug box fixture for rapid production of earthworm eggs, harvest the eggs from the boxes once every thirty days, and use the increase to impregnate large compost beds for soil-building and for development of vast numbers of earthworms. In harvesting the increase from the culture boxes, it is not necessary to complete the work on a particular date. The incubation period of the egg-capsules is from fourteen to twenty-one days; therefore, if the harvesting operations are carried out every twenty-one to thirty days, practically all the increase is recovered.

I present two designs for large compost culture beds Figs. 8, 9, and 10, Plates V and VI, and the more complicated design illustrated by pictures and detailed construction plans of the 'Earthmaster' culture bed shown in Figs. 11, 12, and 13. The plan with posts set in the ground is the simplest and most practical for the average earthworm farmer.

Variation in Size

In the knock-down construction, the size of the bed may be made larger or smaller as desired by the particular individual, to suit the available space and the extent of the land to be eventually impregnated. The important point to note is the way the 2 inches by 4 inches posts are spaced to make the interlocking corners. As will be seen from Fig. 8, the bed is constructed of

2 inch by 4 inch posts and 1 inch by 6 inch planking. No nails are used. The side members of the bed, beginning at the bottom, are set in place one at a time, followed by the end member, which interlocks between to hold the side members in place. Pressure of the compost material keeps all members in place. The compost is built up layer by layer.

Bottom and Drainage (see Fig. 9)

In composting with earthworms, good drainage is of prime importance. To accomplish this, place on the ground as bottom of the bed a layer of four to six inches of coarse sand or gravel, evenly spread, and on top of this place a layer of 1 inch by 6 inch boards, spaced apart about one-half to one inch. This makes the bed mole-proof. Also one main purpose of the bottom boards is to allow unloading of the finished compost with a shovel, without digging into the sand layer which is placed there for permanent drainage. In unloading the broken-down compost, the end members of this culture bed may be pried out one at a time, thus exposing one open end of the bed and allowing the shovelling of the contents of bed into a wheelbarrow or other carrying device for distribution to flower-beds, lawn, or other place of final disposition.

Depth of Bed

While the width and length of the bed may be varied, larger or smaller, as desired, the depth should be maintained at about twenty-four inches. Earthworms are air-breathing animals and must have plenty of air for best results. A depth of about two feet allows for good aeration at all times. Also, in watering a culture bed of this depth it is not difficult to keep the entire contents of the bed thoroughly moist from top to bottom. This is very important in securing best results in earthworm culture. Originally, as I mentioned, earthworms were water animals and their bodies have a very high water content. Any lack of water slows down their activity and reduces productivity of capsules. Beds should not be flooded, but, let it be emphasized again, the contents should be kept thoroughly moist though not soggy. Experience will soon teach how to maintain the best degree of moisture.

EARTHWORM CULTURE

Cover and Shade

In the detailed construction plan I have not shown any cover. A suitable cover, in easily removable sections, should be provided to protect the contents of the bed from flooding rains and to provide shade and darkness. Worms work best in shade and darkness. Rain water is very fine for the worms, so long as the contents of the bed are not flooded. If a good shade tree is conveniently located, the bed can be placed, preferably, on the north side of the tree. This keeps the culture bed as cool as possible during the hot summer months. Worms should not be exposed to hot sunshine directly. However, they are the most active when kept at summer temperatures of from sixty to eighty degrees. The greatest production of capsules will take place in warm earth.

Moisture Conservation

For moisture conservation and to prevent surface drying out, I alway use on top of the compost surface a layer of old tow sacks or burlap. Old feed bags, potato sacks, or other porous material can be used. The bed can be watered through this cover material without disturbing the surface of the compost. The cover material acts as a water-break and spreader, so that, if you water with a hose or sprinkler-head, the worms and surface of the compost are not disturbed by the force of the water stream. It is always best to use a sprinkler-head on the garden hose, as this distributes the water to better advantage, without flooding.

Garbage Disposal and Waste Utilization

All kitchen waste (garbage) is perfect earthworm food and may be disposed of as it accumulates, spreading it on the compost layer by layer. I always spread the garbage evenly over the surface of the bed and then add a thin layer of sifted topsoil on top of the garbage to absorb odours and furnish a base of soil for combining with the vegetable and other matter. The worms consume and combine everything, the final product being rich, black topsoil for potting or other use. Lawn clippings, leaves, small prunings, all trimmings from the vegetable gardens, such

101

as cabbage leaves, lettuce, or other organic material, can be used in the compost, adding it layer by layer and mixing in enough topsoil or subsoil to prevent heating. In composting with earthworms, it is highly important to mix the compost with enough earth to prevent the development of a high degree of heat. This is also one of the main reasons for keeping the culture bed shallow in depth. Deep piles of compost should be avoided, as they may develop intense heat in the deeper layers, enough to destroy animal life, a fact that should always be borne in mind. A liberal amount of manure mixed into compost is a very great advantage.

Intensive Production of Earthworms

Where a rich compost is provided, a culture bed eight feet long, four feet wide and two feet deep will easily support a population of *fifty thousand* domesticated earthworms. Once such a culture bed is fully impregnated and developed from a lug box basis, it is no problem further to develop earthworm culture. In starting additional culture beds, or establishing large compost beds in the open, I simply take a liberal portion of compost from the old culture bed—a wheelbarrow load or more —with such worms and capsules as it may contain—and use this as a starter for the new composting operation. This start will quickly impregnate the new compost, and by the time the bed is full there will be an adequate worm population to break it down quickly into fertile topsoil.

I wish to emphasize at this point that I am laying down certain general principles for earthworm culture. I offer definite plans for culture boxes, culture beds, and so on. However, each earthworm culturist should experiment and develop plans of his own. Any kind of box, container, or culture bed will serve, provided that it has good drainage and is kept shaded and moist. The plans I have set forth have been found, through long experience, to be good. By following a successful plan that has already been tested, the beginner will avoid many mistakes. On the other hand, if no experimenting is carried out, new and better methods will not be discovered.

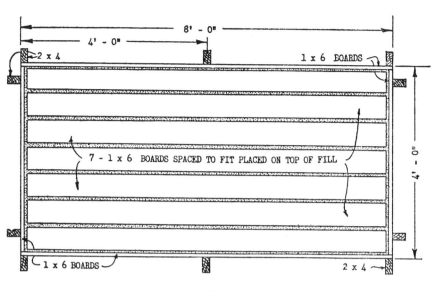

FIG. 8.   Utility culture bed
(*Detailed plan of earthworm culture bed*)

GROUND PLAN
('*Knockdown*' construction)

Boards are laid on top of sand and gravel fill. Makes bed mole-proof. Provides easy shovelling surface for emptying bed, without disturbing sand fill. Improves drainage and aeration

PRACTICAL UTILITY

This bed is a most practical, all-purpose culture bed. While the depth should be kept at two feet, the length and breadth may be varied to suit individual needs. I use lug box culture for rapid production of earthworm egg-capsules. I take the increase and impregnate larger culture beds, such as illustrated, for soil-building and for development of vast numbers of earthworms. This construction provides an excellent unit for household garbage disposal and for general composting of all kinds of organic waste—manures, grass clippings, leaves, etc.

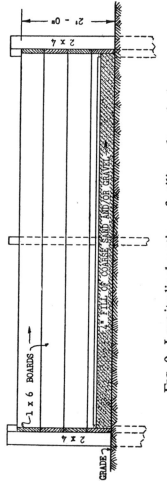

Fig. 9. Longitudinal section of utility culture bed

DRAINAGE

A layer of sand and gravel in bottom, with planking on top, provides good drainage and aeration

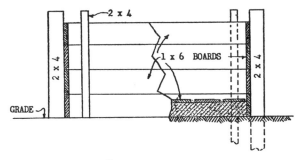

INTERLOCKING

Corner and end posts are set in ground so as to provide interlocking members. No nails are used. For easy emptying, end members may be prized out one at a time, leaving one end open for shovelling

Perspective View

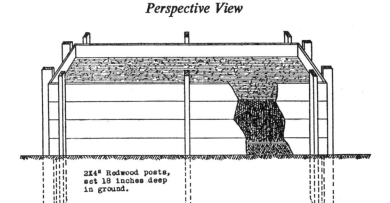

AERATION

The sand fill in bottom with space between side and end members provides plenty of air, with good drainage, for the airbreathing earthworms

FIG. 10.   Partial end view, cross-section and perspective view of utility culture bed

105

XI

EARTHMASTER EARTHWORM CULTURE BED

FOR INTENSIVE PROPAGATION OF DOMESTICATED EARTHWORMS

The Earthmaster Culture Bed is presented as a complete basic unit for conveniently developing and handling approximately 10,000 mature domesticated earthworms. In addition to its practical efficiency may be mentioned simplicity of construction, low material cost, strength, durability, and accessibility. With the superstructure and cover (see last three photographs on Plate VI), it may be used without any other housing. However, where the bed can be shaded under a shed, lath house, tree, or other shelter, the superstructure may be left off (see 2–3 on Plate V).

The V-shaped construction of the compost compartment (see 8–9 on Plate VI) embraces the basic principle of the Earthmaster Culture Bed. It allows perfect aeration and drainage, both very necessary in the successful propagation of the air-breathing domesticated earthworms. On account of the V-shape, when the bed is watered the water flows downward along the side members, gradually becoming concentrated in the narrow portion at the bottom. Then, through capillary attraction, the moisture rises through the centre toward the top. Thus the entire mass of compost is kept uniformly moist throughout.

Years of experience have abundantly demonstrated that it is much better to maintain a battery of medium-sized units which can be completely serviced in rotation, day by day, rather than large culture units which may have to be left partly ser-

106

viced, after a day's work. For this reason, the standard unit described in this chapter has been adopted and advocated in the Earthmaster System. The complete unit, including cover and superstructure, stands 36 inches high and 36 inches square.

The primary purpose of maintaining a culture bed is to provide an easy and convenient method for harvesting earthworm egg-capsules for impregnation of additional culture beds for breeding purposes, or for impregnation of compost heaps, flower-pots, lawns, gardens, orchards, or farms. Also, in intensive production of domesticated earthworms, it is well to protect the breeders from mixing with native earthworms. With Earthmaster Culture Beds, the pure cultures of domesticated earthworms may be maintained intact from mixing.

MATERIALS CUT TO DIMENSION

Timber:

Oregon pine, hemlock, or other available timber.

Corner Posts:

4 pieces 2 inches by 4 inches, 36 inches long. Variation: If superstructure is not desired (see Plate V, 3), make posts 30 inches long.

Frame:

10 pieces 1 inch by 6 inches, 36 inches long. 2 pieces 1 inch by 4 inches, 36 inches long.

Bottom of Compost Compartment:

2 pieces 1 inch by 6 inches, $33\frac{1}{2}$ inches long, 2 pieces of lath, $33\frac{1}{2}$ inches long.

Removable Sides of Compost Compartment:

10 pieces 1 inch by 6 inches, 20 inches long. 2 pieces 1 inch by 4 inches, 20 inches long. Each side requires 5 pieces 1 inch by 6 inches plus 1 piece 1 inch by 4 inches.

End Panels:

10 pieces 1 inch by 6 inches, 24 inches long. Note: 5 pieces

used in each end, spaced $\frac{1}{4}$ inch apart, with 1 inch space between the corner posts and end members of panel.

Sub-Surface Divider:

11 pieces lath (ordinary plasterer's lath), 33 inches long with two end lath 30 inches long. Space between lath about width of lath. (See 7 and 9 on Plate VI.)

Primary Cover (Plate VI, 10):

A light frame, $32\frac{1}{2}$ inches long by 32 inches wide, made of lath and 1 inch by 2 inch material and covered with a piece of gunny sack (tow sack, sugar sack, burlap or other porous material). Note: When cover is in place, contents of bed may be watered through the cover with hose sprinkler or sprinkler can. Cover acts as a water spreader.

Supercover (Plate VI, 10, 11 and 12):

A light frame 36 inches by 36 inches square, made of 1 inch by 2 inch or other light material, covered with gunny sack. In addition, four side walls are made by tacking an opened gunny sack (see Plate VI, 12) to each of the four sides of the frame, leaving one edge to hang free. Thus, when not in use, the side curtains may be folded back on top of the frame as in Plate V, 1. Or for protection against excessive summer heat, or for protection against cold, the walls may be dropped down as in Plate VI, 12. For protection against flooding rains, an extra cover should be provided, made of a frame covered with roofing paper. All covers should be of light construction, so that they may be readily lifted off when the bed is serviced, or for other attention.

Special Emphasis:

Study all photographs carefully for correct assembly and nailing. If properly assembled and nailed together, the bed will not become 'wobbly' or pull apart.

EARTHMASTER EARTHWORM CULTURE BED

(All references are to Plates V and VI)

Photograph No. 1

Work bench, with materials cut to dimensions.

Photograph No. 2. (View without superstructure)

End panels. Left shows inside of panel, base-sill flush with bottom of corner posts. Right shows outside of panel, top rail 30 inches above ground, bottom rail 6 inches above ground. Material for each panel: 2 corner posts, 2 inches by 4 inches, 30 inches long, 3–1 inch by 6 inches, 36 inches long; 5–1 inch by 6 inches, 24 inches long. (Note: Photographs No. 2 and No. 3 show view without superstructure. If superstructure is desired, corner posts will be 36 inches long, as in photograph No. 4.)

Photograph No. 3. (View without superstructure)

Frame assembled with bottom boards leaning against the corner. Note lath strips tacked on each edge of bottom boards, 2 inches from edge. Removable side-wall members abut against the lath strips on bottom (see photograph No. 8). Note position of frame rails—side top-rails *inside*; end top-rails *outside*. Note that position of base-sills is reversed—side-sill *outside*; end-sill *inside*. Note that top side-rail is composed of 1 inch by 6 inches above, 1 inch by 4 inches below it.

Photograph No. 4. (View with superstructure)

Frame showing corner posts projecting 6 inches above top rails. Note that bottom boards are centred, with ends supported on the end base-sills. Note that side-rails are nailed to *flat* of corner posts; end-rails nailed to *edge* of corner posts.

Photograph No. 5

Compost compartment partially assembled, with three of the removable side-wall members leaning against frame. Note space of ¼ inch between members. Uniform spacing between members is maintained by driving a roofing nail into the edge of each member, leaving head of nail projecting ¼ inch. This spacing is

THE EARTHWORM UNDER CONTROL

for aeration and to allow for swelling of the wet wood. A one-inch space is allowed between the upright members of the end panels and the corner posts to allow for nailing of top side-rails on inside of posts (see photographs No. 8–9 for this detail).

Photograph No. 6

Side view, showing compost compartment completely assembled. See photographs No. 8–9 for details of inside.

Photograph No. 7

View showing sub-surface divider, 33 inches by 30 inches. Space between lath is about the width of a lath. When divider is in place (see photograph No. 9), the compost compartment is divided into large lower chamber for permanent earthworm burrows, with a shallow upper space, 6 inches deep, which forms the feeding ground and egg-capsule 'nest'.

Photograph No. 8

View looking down into compost compartment. Note the ¾ inch spacing between all members. Note removable side members, with lower ends resting against the lath strips on bottom, the top ends resting against side-rails 6 inches below top edge. When the compost compartment is filled, pressure of the material holds side-walls firmly in place. By inserting a 'pry' on the outside of the compost compartment, between the side-wall and top rail, it is a simple matter to pry a member up and release the bottom end, removing the members one at a time. Thus two or three, or all, of the side-wall members may be removed, allowing the material in the compost compartment to be conveniently removed from below. The permanent breeding compost is changed two or three times a year and replaced by fresh material. The 'egg-nest' material above the sub-surface divider (see photograph No. 9) is worked over frequently in harvesting capsules and castings.

Photograph No. 9

View showing sub-surface divider in place, 6 inches below top, resting on the upper ends of side-wall members. The chamber below the divider is filled with earthworm culture compost and forms the permanent burrowing ground for approximately 10,000 mature breeding worms. Material of lower chamber is changed two or three times a year. The space above the divider, six inches deep, is filled with well-prepared culture compost and forms the feeding, breeding and egg-capsule nest. The material in the egg nest is worked over every two or three weeks, the eggs harvested, castings sifted out, and new material added. As earthworm eggs hatch in from fourteen to twenty-one days from the time they are produced, all increase is recovered by working the egg nest every two or three weeks. Capsules are used for establishing additional breeding beds, or for impregnating compost heaps, or for impregnating the soil in garden, flower-pots, nursery, orchard, farm, etc.

Photograph No. 10

View showing primary cover in place, with supercover alongside. Note that the primary cover is used directly above compost compartment, resting on edges of top rails. This cover is made by tacking tow sack over a light frame. Contents of bed may be watered through this cover, using sprinkler hose or can. Cover acts as a water break and spreads water uniformly over surface of bed.

Photograph No 11

View showing supercover in place, with side-walls folded on top. This cover is made by tacking an opened tow sack on a light frame, 36 inches by 36 inches square. Side-walls are made by tacking one edge of an opened tow sack on each of the four sides of the frame, leaving one edge of sack free to hang down as a side-wall, as shown in photograph No. 12. Purpose of the supercover is for extra shade and protection during summer season, and as protection against cold. Contents of bed may be watered through the top of supercover, same as through the primary cover. A light rain cover should be made of roofing paper or other material, to protect the contents of the bed against flooding rains. The supercover should be made light so that it can be readily lifted off for servicing of bed.

Photograph No. 12

View showing supercover, with side-walls lowered. Worms work best and multiply rapidly when kept moderately warm. An even temperature approaching summer heat is best. In extra hot weather, the supercover as illustrated acts as a 'desert cooler', when sprayed with water occasionally. In the advancing coolness of autumn weather, the cover acts as a wind-break and protects the bed from excessive chill. As pointed out above, where other shade is available, such as a shed, lath house, garage, barn, basement—or even the north side of a tree —the superstructure may be dispensed with. However, if the culture bed is maintained in the open, a rain-cover should always be provided to protect the bed from flooding. It should always be borne in mind that earthworms work best in the dark and that plenty of shade is essential to best results in intensive propagation.

IMPORTANCE OF CONTROLLED PRODUCTION

In the intensive propagation and use of domesticated earthworms, it is essential that egg-capsule production be maintained under perfect control, so that an adequate source of capsules be available at all times. Therefore, at least one unit of breeders should be maintained under perfect control, depending on how much land is to be impregnated. If large acreage is to be impregnated, then a battery of units will be required. Another important consideration is that of keeping the breeding strain of domesticated earthworms free from mixing with native earthworms. Domesticated earthworms have been produced through selective feeding and breeding of native earthworms for certain favourable characteristics for intensive propagation. In the Earthmaster Culture Bed, the breeders are protected from mixing. With one or more Earthmaster 'egg-nests' for capsule production, large compost piles may be impregnated and culture material from such piles be used for establishing numerous earthworm colonies in lawn, garden, orchard or fields. For building up a battery of Earthmaster Culture Beds, the entire increase from the original unit may be used and within a few months the breeding units may be increased to a point where it is possible to impregnate acreage. For small set-ups, such as potted plants, or small yard or garden, a single breeding unit is all that is required.

The Earthmaster Culture Bed is designed to house approximately 10,000 mature breeding earthworms, for maximum production of egg-capsules and for convenient harvesting. In use, the compost compartment (see photograph No. 8) is filled with culture compost to the top of the side-wall members, which will be within six inches of the top of the bed.

Mixing of Compost

The mixing of the compost exactly right will come with experience. The approximate composition of good earthworm culture compost is one-third animal manure (horse, chicken, cow, rabbit, sheep, or other domestic animal or fowl); one-third vegetable matter (grass clippings, leaves, kitchen refuse, such as vegetable trimmings, coffee grounds, tea-leaves, cooked or raw left-overs, etc.—in short, garbage); one-third good topsoil, well sifted. All green stuff is especially desirable for capsule production, such as cabbage, lettuce, beet greens, carrot greens, etc. If the manure is fresh, so much the better, but more topsoil should be used in this case to prevent heating. Soil is added to absorb odours, prevent heating and to add 'body' to the earthworm castings. The material may be thoroughly mixed with a shovel or fork.

Screening Materials

The more finely broken up the material, the better. A feed grinder may be utilized for cutting up vegetable matter. The topsoil should be screened through a half-inch mesh, or finer, to remove small stones, hard clods, etc. However, good results may be obtained by mixing the materials coarse and allowing the earthworms to break it up. Production of potting material is greatly accelerated by breaking up the material in advance for quick consumption by earthworms. If one has the time, it pays to prepare the compost in a finely divided state.

Wetting Down the Compost

After filling the compost compartment, material should be thoroughly wetted down and allowed to settle. Keep adding material and wetting it down until the compartment is filled to within six inches of the top with well-settled compost; then put the sub-surface divider in place as shown in photograph No. 9. Thus you will have a space above the divider about six inches deep, with the large mass of compost below the divider to form the permanent burrowing ground of the breeders.

Purpose of the Sub-Surface Divider

The sub-surface divider is used so that, in the process of frequent egg-harvesting from the material on top of the divider, the permanent burrowing ground of the earthworms will not be disturbed or broken up.

Impregnating the Earthmaster Culture Bed

After the sub-surface divider is in place (photograph No. 9), the space above it is filled with especially well-prepared culture compost of the same materials as that in the lower chamber, and thoroughly wetted down and allowed to drain and settle. After settling, the material should be at a level from one to two inches below the edge of top rails. The entire bed should now be moist throughout, but not soggy. In the first wetting down, water is used freely and allowed to drain off. Subsequent waterings are not so generous—just well sprinkled to keep contents moist, but not soggy. The prepared bed is now impregnated with 3,000 Domesticated Earthworm Egg-Capsules, by burying them in the surface of the compost one to two inches deep. Distribute the capsules over the entire surface, using capsules and material in which they are packed. Do not try to separate capsules from packing material—just dump entire contents on surface of the compost, lightly rake it over the surface of bed and then cover with a layer of fine compost to a depth of one to two inches

EARTHMASTER EARTHWORM CULTURE BED

For conserving the moisture and keeping the surface of the compost from drying out too much, a layer of wet tow sack should be placed on the surface. This should not be removed during the development period of sixty to ninety days. The water will soak right through it. The primary and supercover (photographs No. 10, 11, and 12) are now put in place.

Care of the Bed

Contents of the bed should not be disturbed for from sixty to ninety days from date of planting of capsules, except for watering as often as is necessary to keep it moist, or for occasional inspection to determine the condition of moisture. In cool weather, one good watering each week is sufficient. In hot summer weather, a light sprinkling every day or two may be necessary to keep the surface from drying out, with a good watering once a week. Experience will show how often to water to keep contents damp. The bed should never be allowed to dry out.

Hatching of Capsules

Earthmaster Domesticated Earthworm Egg-Capsules will hatch out in from fourteen to twenty-one days. From one to as many as twenty worms per egg may develop. They will probably average three or four worms per capsule. It is estimated that from 9,000 to 12,000 worms will develop from 3,000 capsules. Earthworms mature and begin to breed in from sixty to ninety days, according to moisture and temperature; thus production is quickly established. Under favourable conditions, domesticated earthworms may pass an egg-capsule every seven to ten days, so that the increase is extremely rapid. After sixty days from impregnation, the surface compost should be examined to a depth of three or four inches for capsules. If capsules are found, the routine of harvesting may be started.

HARVESTING THE INCREASE

Egg-Capsules and Castings

As earthworm egg-capsules hatch in fourteen to twenty-one days from the time they are deposited, it is evident that if the material in the egg-nest is removed or worked over every two to three weeks, the capsules which have been deposited during this period will be recovered. Earthworms come to the surface to deposit their eggs and castings. They feed mainly near the surface, especially at night, or if the bed is kept shaded and dark. For this reason, the surface should be kept moist and well-covered. A damp tow sack on the surface forms a good cover for darkness and dampness. When disturbed by light and vibration, or if too hot, the worms will withdraw into their permanent burrows deeper in the culture bed.

Removing Contents of Egg-nest

Before removing the material from the nest, it should be raked into a cone-shaped pile in the centre of the bed (covers laid aside) and allowed partly to dry out. When disturbed or exposed to light, the worms will rapidly work downward to escape from the light and drying. In a few minutes after exposure, an inch or more of the surface may be removed for screening. Two small hand-screen boxes should be provided, one with half-inch screen to remove the coarser material which is to be mixed with new compost. The finer material, containing the eggs, will pass through the coarse screen. Next, the material from the first screening is passed through a quarter-inch screen. The earthworm castings, with the egg-capsules, will now be found in the very fine screenings. The coarser material that does not pass through the quarter-inch screen is remixed with new compost. The harvest thus proceeds, the material being removed layer by layer, down to the sub-surface divider. The mature breeder-worms will continue to work downward and take refuge in their permanent burrows below the sub-surface divider.

Reloading the Egg-nest

Fresh, fine compost, the same as the original material, is now mixed with the screenings from the harvest, and the egg-nest is filled, wetted down, and covered, just as the original bed was prepared. The routine of harvesting is carried out every two or three weeks. With simple care as outlined, by using the increase to build additional culture beds, a battery of producing units can very quickly be built up and thus a controlled production apparatus for impregnating extensive ground, or for commercial use, will be established.

Use of Egg-Capsules and Earthworm Castings

The material harvested from the Earthmaster Culture Bed is composed of earthworm castings, fine particles of compost, and also contains the egg-capsules. It is not necessary to pick out the capsules in order to use them. That is only necessary where they are to be counted and sold. The harvested material is used for potting plants, in flower-beds, around trees, in the yard or garden. Wherever a handful of this material is used, a numerous earthworm colony is established, gradually to increase and impregnate the earth in an ever-widening circle from the original point of impregnation. Thus, by seeding the flowerpots, flower-beds, the earth around shrubs and trees, yard and garden, an adequate earthworm population is rapidly built up to enrich and condition the earth for all time to come.

Composting for Increase

The Earthmaster Breeding Units are maintained as a controlled supply of capsules from the pure strain of domesticated earthworms. But this does not mean that the culture beds are the only source for impregnating the earth. For extensive impregnation of grounds, all household garbage, lawn clippings, leaves, prunings, etc., should be carefully composted at some well-shaded location and thoroughly impregnated with earthworm egg-capsules. A numerous earthworm population will rapidly develop in the compost, digesting the material quickly and turning it into the most choice topsoil for potting and other uses. This composted material can be used liberally, wherever needed, and earthworm colonies will be established wherever it is used. By reserving part of the compost for new beds, reseeding of the compost is not necessary. Soon a very great supply of earthworms will be developed in the composting operations. All garden books give instructions on building compost, which is a very simple matter.

THE EARTHWORM UNDER CONTROL

For extensive acreage, many tons of compost should be built up and maintained as culture beds for earthworms, using the material after it has been transformed by the earthworms, with all that it contains of worms, capsules, and castings, for impregnating the earth wherever it is desired to establish an adequate earthworm population.

DOMESTICATED EARTHWORMS

All earthworms are valuable as soil-builders, as they function in the same manner. There are hundreds of varieties of native earthworms, with varying characteristics and habits. Some are very prolific. Some multiply slowly. Some varieties feed on a very limited range of material. Others consume practically everything in the nature of animal and vegetable waste. Some are adjusted to a very limited range of soil acidity. Others adapt themselves to a wide range of soils. Through selective breeding and feeding, domesticated earthworms, adapted to intensive propagation and use, have been developed. They are very prolific, adapt themselves to a wide range of soil acidity, thrive on practically all the biological end-products of life, both animal waste as well as all vegetable matter, and are much less migratory than most native earthworms. When a colony is established, they remain and spread slowly to the surrounding environment.

In intensive earthworm culture, we create a favourable environment and use domesticated earthworms which have the necessary characteristics for propagation in high concentrations. An ordinary lug box, six inches deep and about eighteen inches square, will accommodate 500 to 600 breeders. Under desirable breeding conditions, it is estimated that one worm may increase to more than six hundred within a year, starting from a single egg-capsule. After adequate culture beds have been established, it is a simple matter to build up the cultures to a point where biological soil-building on a substantial scale is possible. A single Earthmaster Culture Bed, impregnated with 3,000 Domesticated Earthworm Egg-Capsules, forms the foundation for a fascinating hobby, or a profitable and satisfying home industry.

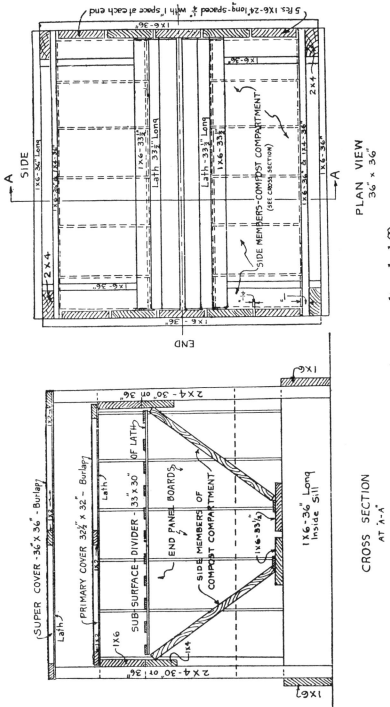

Fig. 11. Earthmaster culture bed (I)

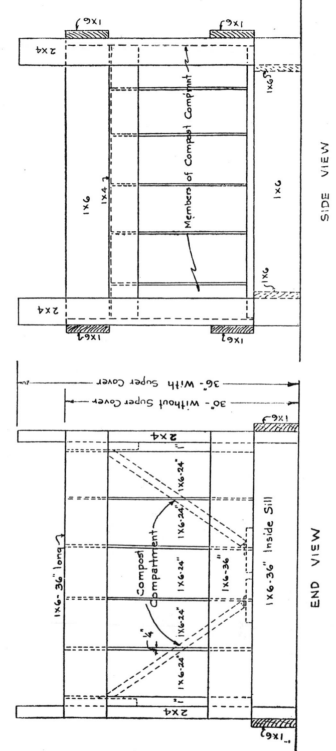

FIG. 12. Earthmaster culture bed (II)

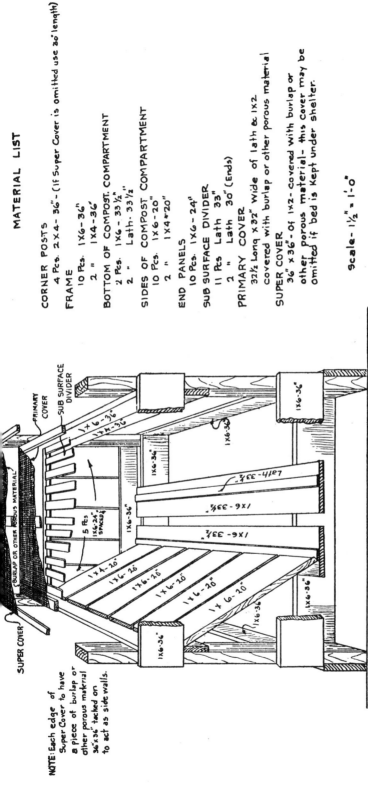

MATERIAL LIST

CORNER POSTS
   4 Pcs. 2×4–36". (If Super Cover is omitted use 30" length)

FRAME
   10 Pcs. 1×6–36"
   2 " 1×4–36'

BOTTOM OF COMPOST. COMPARTMENT
   2 Pcs. 1×6– 33½"
   2 " Lath- 33½

SIDES OF COMPOST COMPARTMENT
   10 Pcs. 1×6–20"
   2 " 1×4"20"

END PANELS
   10 Pcs. 1×6–24"

SUB SURFACE DIVIDER
   11 Pcs Lath 33"
   2 " Lath 30"(Ends)

PRIMARY COVER
   32½ Long × 32" wide of lath & 1×2 covered with burlap or other porous material

SUPER COVER
   36" × 36"- of 1×2- covered with burlap or other porous material- this cover may be omitted if bed is Kept under shelter.

Scale- 1½" = 1'-0"

NOTE: Each edge of Super Cover to have a piece of burlap or other porous material 36"×36" tacked on to act as side walls.

SECTIONAL PERSPECTIVE VIEW
Showing Details of Assembling

FIG. 13. Earthmaster culture bed (III)

(*Working drawings Earthmaster culture bed copyright 1942 by Thomas J. Barrett*)

XII

EARTHWORM TILLAGE

We shall define 'earthworm tillage' as a general term covering methods adopted to encourage the maximum development of native earthworm population in the land. And as a practical part of earthworm tillage methods, we should include intensive propagation of earthworms for 'seeding' the land with egg-capsules, not only to accelerate the development of a numerous worm population in the shortest possible time, but also as a method for utilizing every possible organic waste material in building topsoil to be used as a top-dressing in garden, orchard and farm.

In our chapter on 'My Grandfather's Earthworm Farm', the methods described would be classed as earthworm tillage. In the chapter on 'Orcharding with Earthworms', we touched on earthworm tillage methods as followed by Mr. Hinckley in his citrus orchard. We should say that Edward H. Faulkner's book, *Plowman's Folly*, is primarily an able discussion of earthworm tillage. In fact, the remarkable results reported in that book we should attribute to the fauna of the soil, with very great emphasis placed on the earthworm population. However, the question is not 'to plough or not to plough'; we shall not enter that controversial field. We advise every student of earthworm culture to read carefully *Plowman's Folly*, as well as everything else he can find on organic methods. It is all instruction in earthworm tillage and earthworm culture. Once the basic principles are grasped, a new world of possibilities and instruction is revealed for study and experimentation.

We also recommend as possibly the most important book on basic organic methods Sir Albert Howard's *An Agricultural Testament*.[1] If we were recommending one single book from all books on the subject for earthworm students, we would say,

[1] Oxford University Press, 1940.

EARTHWORM TILLAGE

'read *An Agricultural Testament*' However, once one has started on a study of organic methods, as contrasted with the strictly 'chemical' school of thought, one finds the sources of recorded information almost endless, with the soil itself as a fascinating subject for practical experimentation of never-failing interest.

As an outstanding example of what we mean by 'earthworm tillage', showing the tremendous increase in food production that may take place through use of such methods, we reproduce an article which appeared in the February 1945 issue of *Farm Journal and Farmer's Wife*, under the title, 'Earthworms, 150,000 to the Acre'. This report on the farming methods and results obtained by Mr. Christopher Gallup is a corroboration of the methods which we described in the chapter on 'My Grandfather's Earthworm Farm', but applied to a modern farm with modern machinery.

Incidentally, we have been in correspondence with Mr. Gallup, who is an energetic, aggressive student of modern methods and a successful farmer. In connection with the story of his farm, we quote a few lines from a letter received from him under date of 18th April 1945: 'When we used to get 70 bushel baskets of corn per acre, the borers just raised Cain with it; but when our yield had been stepped up to 196 baskets per acre, the borers practically dropped out of the picture.' In another letter from Mr. Gallup under date of 3rd June 1945, he remarks: 'Saturday we finished putting 37 truck loads of hay into the barn from two fields that produced only 21 truck loads last year. No manure or fertilizer was used in making the difference.'

EARTHWORMS: 150,000 TO THE ACRE
By WILLIAMS HAYNES

(This article reproduced by permission of Farm Journal and Farmer's Wife *and by permission of Williams Haynes)*

Fishermen each season dangle millions of earthworms in likely waters. No other bait enjoys such popularity with anglers. The fish may, or may not, hold similar views.

THE EARTHWORM UNDER CONTROL

Christopher Gallup looks at the earthworm as bait for bigger crops. More earthworms, he contends, mean higher fertility.

In evidence he offers a yield of 196 bushel baskets of ear corn, in contrast to the 80 bushels his earlier methods produced. His swarming earthworms annually leave more than eight tons of their casts per acre. (The cast is the deposit after the worm digests the vegetable and mineral material which it eats.)

Then Gallup points to the chemical analysis of these casts. Compared with other topsoil, they contain five times as much nitrogen, seven times as much phosphorus, eleven times as much potash, three times as much magnesium.

How does one persuade the earthworms to multiply? Feed them, says Gallup; feed them trash and organic matter. His method is to work everything possible into the top six inches of soil, where, in the lower four inches, the worms do most of their living.

Gallup's farm lies among stony hills of eastern Connecticut. Two hundred and seventy years ago when King Philip and his Narragansett braves, in 1675, took to the war-path and ravaged that corner of Connecticut, a forebear of Christopher Gallup already had some of the farm cleared.

Fifteen years ago, determined to be as successful as a farmer, as he had previously been in a Hartford insurance company, Gallup began operating the family's ancient homestead.

He says, 'I went into our little fields with a heavy plough hooked to a 20 h.p. caterpillar tractor, determined to give that old land the works. I ploughed deep. I put on lime and commercial fertilizer. I did everything the experts advised. I firmly believed with all its stones our New England soil was good soil. But the best I could get was 80 bushels of corn, in spite of a lot of fertilizer and hard work.' Ultimately, Gallup hit on his answer—the spring-tooth harrow plus earthworms.

No one, Gallup says, knows all about earthworms. They eat and digest both decaying vegetation and soil itself. Their tunnels carry air and water into the ground. Exactly what happens in the gizzards between their suction mouths and the fertile casts is yet to be found out.

A scientists' count indicates that in Gallup's best fields as many as 150,000 worms inhabit each acre. A western student believes the worm population on an acre could be increased to ten times that number, enough to bring two and half tons of digested material to the surface each twenty-four hours. That's a lot of plant food, in any language.

Gallup figures that four years are needed to build up the worm numbers. Harrowing the trash in helps in the first year to create their food supply. The second year the breeding stock begins to congregate, the third it multiplies. By the fourth the worms are heaving up subsoil in quantity.

'Nowadays', he explains, 'we get out with the tooth-harrow as soon as the frost is out. That is a good three weeks earlier than we could use a plough, and a couple of weeks before the land could be worked with a disc harrow. Grass and perennial weeds can then be killed with surprising ease.'

Gallup's cultivating method is to set the teeth of the harrow at the most shallow notch, and to go over the field several times. Then he spreads his manure and promptly harrows it in. After each heavy spring rain he harrows again, both ways, each time lowering the teeth one notch.

Frequently people ask, 'What about the trash? Doesn't it bunch up?' 'And', they add, 'aren't your fields "dirty", and isn't that litter an A1 incubator for pests?'

Gallup says 'No' to both questions. He is, in fact, strongly of the view that 'earthworm tillage' keeps down the corn borers.

Early in the spring before a bit of new growth starts, the trash—even heavy trash like corn stubble—is quite tender after having been softened by frost and snow. Warm sun and spring rains, and the worms, hurry its decay. Even at the first harrowing, Gallup says the trash almost never bunches, and by planting time it has disappeared.

When he brings a piece of sod into cultivation, Gallup cuts the sod with a disc harrow late in July, and rakes crossways with the spring-tooth. Next he manures heavily and rakes in lightly with the spring-tooth. After five cultivations, he sows rye, and is ready by spring for his regular procedure.

You notice at once that he cultivates both in preparation and in regular tillage more often than usual. However, the tractor in high speed can harrow five or six times as fast as plough or cultivator can travel.

While the soil is still loose the corn is drilled in rows with a planter and cultivator with hiller-discs that throw a heavy ridge over the drilled seed. This, he believes, gives extra moisture for germination. Four to eight days later the cultivator with weeder teeth in front breaks down the ridge, destroying any young weeds. When the corn is a foot high the hiller-disc again throws back the ridge. Tractor cultivation continues until the corn is two feet high.

Gallup does not use hybrid seed. This spring he will plant selected seed from his 1944 crop, which will be detasselled for growing seed. He will also plant selected corn from his 1943 crop for the pollen rows in his seed plot. He thinks this avoids the disadvantage of inbreeding and gives vigour.

'Part of the increased yields', says Gallup, 'is due to this kind of seed selection. But the method of cultivation which brings on more earthworms is mainly responsible.' Maybe he has something.

XIII

TECHNICAL DISCUSSION; FACTS, FIGURES AND REFERENCES

In this book, so far, we have purposely avoided technical terms and discussion. We set out to create a mental picture of the importance of the earthworm in nature and to point the way to harnessing the earthworm in the intensive service of man. In our handling of the subject, we have made broad claims for the value of earthworms, some of the claims supported, and some unsupported except by our own experimental findings. For those who are not informed fully on the subject, and for those who might seriously question much of the foregoing we are glad to reproduce a highly valuable report recently released for publication by the Connecticut Agricultural Experiment Station. In this report on 'The Chemical Composition of Earthworm Casts', H. A. Lunt and H. G. M. Jacobson have revealed in a few well-written pages the scientific basis of all the claims made for earthworms by popular writers, including the author of this book. Also, the inclusion of this authoritative report will satisfy the technical and strictly scientific students who might otherwise question, or even throw aside, this book as not worth their attention.

In the last paragraph of the Lunt and Jacobson report, under the heading of 'Discussion', we find the statement: 'Whether or not it is practicable deliberately to increase the worm population is another question and one which still lacks an answer.' We believe that *Harnessing the Earthworm* is a very definite answer to this question, and in the affirmative; although the contents of this book, with the instances and experiments cited, are obviously not familiar to the writers of 'The Chemical Composition of Earthworm Casts'. The same comment applies to the concluding statement in the 'Summary' by Doctors Lunt and Jacobson, which reads: 'Conditions favourable to the worms, however, are at the same time favourable to plant growth, and quantitative measurements under field conditions of the part the worms play in crop production have not as yet been obtained.' As a further comment on this last quotation, I may point out that the field soil samples reported on in this bulletin were collected from the farm of Mr. Christopher M. Gallup. We consider that the experience of Mr. Gallup in increasing his production of corn from 80 bushels per acre to an average of 196 bushels per acre is at least one startling example of what can be accomplished through 'earthworm tillage'.

In the following pages we give the report of Doctors Lunt and Jacobson in its entirety, with the valuable list of reference books at the end of the report.

Reprinted from *Soil Science*, Vol. 58, No. 5, November 1944

THE CHEMICAL COMPOSITION OF EARTHWORM CASTS[1]

H. A. LUNT and H. G. M. JACOBSON[2]
(*Connecticut Agricultural Experiment Station*)
Received for publication 22nd July 1944

Many years ago Gilbert White,[3] and later, Darwin (2) stressed the value of earthworms to agriculture, and agronomists and foresters as well as many practical farmers and gardeners have recognized the improvement in the physical condition of the soil brought about by these inhabitants. Little has been done, how-

[1] Contribution from the department of soils, Connecticut Agricultural Experiment Station, New Haven, Connecticut.

[2] Associate in forest soils and associate agronomist, respectively.

[3] Russell (8) quotes the following from Gilbert White, published in 1777: 'Worms seem to be the great promoters of vegetation, which would proceed but lamely without them, by boring, perforating, and loosening the soil, and rendering it pervious to rains and the fibres of plants, by drawing straws and stalks of leaves and twigs into it; and, most of all, by throwing up such infinite numbers of lumps of earth called worm-casts, which, being their excrement, is a fine manure for grain and grass . . . the earth without worms would soon become cold, hard-bound, and void of fermentation, and consequently sterile.'

ever, to exploit the idea or to 'put the worms to work' on any extensive scale until recently. A number of farmers have adopted what is called 'earthworm tillage' or 'biodynamic farming', the terms not being exactly synonymous but referring to practices which have some features in common. The reported successes of these farming methods have prompted the study of the properties of worm casts in comparison with the soil mass as a whole. No effort was made to obtain quantitative measurements of the amount of cast material thrown up in a year, although a rough estimate was made of the quantity present on the field at the time of sampling.

REVIEW OF LITERATURE

Although several workers have investigated the activities and the benefits of earthworms, only a few data on the composition of the casts have been published. Darwin (2) devoted a whole book to the subject of earthworms but did not include any such data. Hensen (3) found that loss on ignition of worm excrement lining the burrows was 3·3 to 5 per cent, compared with 2·3 per cent for the unworked soil. He also mentioned that Müller reported 24 to 30 per cent loss on ignition for worm excrement in contrast to about 8 per cent for soil. Salisbury (9) found that worm casts had a higher organic matter content than the soil in six cases out of eight. He also reported that the reaction of the casts was usually more nearly neutral than was that of the original soil. Similar findings have been reported by Robertson (7) and are shown in the data of Puh given below. Blanck and Giescke (1) found a marked increase in the nitrifying power of the three different soil types as the result of earthworm activity. Earthworm casts collected from cut-over land on two soil types had higher base-exchange capacities, organic matter, and nitrogen contents than did the unworked soil mass, according to Powers and Bollen (5). They discovered that barley grown in pots produced much higher yields when earthworms were present than when the soil was free of worms.

Robertson (7) has shown that earthworms secrete calcium carbonate concretions in their calciferous glands. Secretion can take place under acid, neutral, or alkaline conditions, provided the worms have access to material containing calcium. He points out, however, that these concretions, which are excreted in the casts, do not affect the reaction of the casts in the least; it is rather the secretions of the gut wall which are responsible for changes in the reaction of the casts. When worms were kept on filter paper or in acid peat, formation of calcite concretions ceased after a week or ten days.

Stöckli (10) studied the effect of earthworms on the soil in ten different places including garden, meadow, and forest soils. He found great variations in their activity from place to place and from season to season. Temperature and moisture were all important; geological origin of the soil was of no consequence. In comparison with the undisturbed soil, the casts and the linings of the tunnels had, in general, higher pH and loss-on-ignition values, higher content of humus soluble in 30 per cent H_2O_2, and higher bacterial count.

Using a non-calcareous loamy clay, not ordinarily occupied by worms, with which were mixed 1 part calcareous sandy soil to 9 parts of the loamy clay, and finely cut leaves and stems of *Latuca sativa*, Puh (6) introduced earthworms (*Pheretima bucculenta*) and left them for two months. At the end of this time the casts covered virtually the whole surface. Her analyses of the soil and of the worm casts at the end of this period were as follows:

	Parent Soil	Worm Casts
pH (non-calcareous loamy clay)	6·2	6·8
pH (non-calcareous loamy clay, with calcareous sand)	6·4	6·7
	8·5	7·4
pH (calcareous loamy clays)	7·8	7·5
	8·0	7·2
Base capacity per 100 gm. (*m.e.*)	21·0	25·5
Exchangeable calcium (CaO) per 100 gm. (*m.e.*)	17·8	17·8
Available phosphorus (*p.p.m.*)	37·3	53·9
Available potassium (*p.p.m.*)	193·0	294·0
Ammonia nitrogen (*p.p.m.*)	33·0	49·0
CaO (*per cent*)	1·95	2·37
Total nitrogen (*per cent*)	0·054	0·151
Organic matter (*per cent*)	1·20	1·52

FACTS, FIGURES AND REFERENCES

Lindquist (4) reports that earthworms increase nitrate production not only by mixing humus with mineral soil and stimulating bacterial activity but also through the decomposition of their own bodies.

AREAS SAMPLED

To obtain more complete data than have been published heretofore, to the knowledge of the writers, samples of casts and of the surrounding soil mass were collected in the autumn of 1942 from both field and forest and were subjected to rather complete analysis.[1] The field samples were obtained in a field of sorghum and soybean stubble and young sweet clover on Earthworm Tillage Farms No. 1,[2] in North Stonington, Connecticut. The 'earthworm tillage' consists essentially in working the stubble and other plant debris into the upper 4 or 5 inches of soil by means of disc and spring-tooth harrows, rather than ploughing under in the conventional manner. Everything possible is done to supply food for the worms in order to increase their number. The field, of approximately 4 acres, was being pastured by ten steers and two milk cows. The soil is principally Hinckley gravelly loam, and the higher portion is classed as belonging to the Gloucester or Plymouth series. Samples were collected at 5-pace intervals along six lines across the field, and each group of line samples was composted into one sample. In each case three kinds of material were taken; first, earthworm casts; second, the adjoining soil mass to a depth of 6 inches; and third, soil at the 8–16-inch level.

The forest soil samples, obtained in four separate areas, consisted of casts; A1 horizon (nearby top $\frac{1}{2}$ to 1 inch soil, not casts); A3 horizon ($1\frac{1}{2}$ to 8-inch layer consisting of the remainder of A and, in some cases, a part of the B horizon); and B horizon (8 to 20 inches, more or less). Locations and descriptions of the areas are as follows:

1. Mt. Carmel State Park, Hamden. Holyoke stony fine sandy

---

[1] Field samples were collected by H. G. M. Jacobson and E. J. Rubins; those from forested areas, by H. A. Lunt and D. B. Downs. Most of the analyses were made by Mr. Rubins.

[2] Property of Christopher M. Gallup.

loam. Mixed hard woods, principally oak with maple and dog-wood. Samples were taken at edge of timber just in the open. Casts were numerous and well defined. (In the woods, casts prevailed, but it would have been difficult to find unworked material.)

2. Middletown, private property. Southington stony fine sandy loam. Principally white oak, with black oak, hickory, sugar maple, and other species. Casts were so numerous it was difficult to be sure of unworked soil. (Subsequent analyses, however, showed a marked difference in properties of the casts as compared with the surrounding soil mass.)

3. Meshomasic State Forest, Portland. Hinsdale stony fine sandy loam. Mixed hardwoods consisting principally of red oak, chestnut oak, white oak, dogwood, and sugar maple. Abundant casts.

4. Middlefield, private property. Southington stony fine sand loam. Mixed hardwoods, consisting of white, red, and chestnut oaks, hickory, sugar maple, dogwood, sassafras, and hemlock. Casts were abundant.

Quantitative measurements of the number of casts produced throughout the year or of the number of earthworms were not attempted, nor was identification of the worms as to species. A rough estimate indicated that, at the time of sampling, the casts in the field numbered approximately three to the square foot and weighed 2 ounces apiece, which amounted to about 129,000 per acre and a weight of 16,000 pounds.

RESULTS

Data pertaining to the analyses of the casts and soil from the cultivated field are given in Table 1. In most cases agreement between samples from several parts of the field was good, and differences between horizons were considerably greater than were differences between samples from the same horizon. In nearly all cases the casts showed higher values than the 0–6-inch layer, which in turn were higher than those of the 8–16-inch depth. Greater differences were found in available phosphorus and exchangeable potassium and magnesium, the increases in

132

FACTS, FIGURES AND REFERENCES

TABLE I

Properties of earthworm casts and of soil from cultivated field
Values given are means of six samples[1] with standard deviations

	Casts		Soil 0-6 in.		Soil 8-16 in.	
	Mean	*SD*	*Mean*	*SD*	*Mean*	*SD*
Total nitrogen (*per cent*)	·353	0·023	0·246	0·048	0·081	0·011
Organic carbon (*per cent*)	05·17	0·24	3·35	0·48	1·11	0·16
Carbon: nitrogen	14·7	0·5	13·8	1·8	13·8	1·7
Loss on ignition (*per cent*)	13·1	0·6	9·8	0·3	4·9	0·4
Nitrate nitrogen (*p.p.m.*)	21·9	6·9	4·7	1·0	1·7	0·6
Available phosphorus (Truog) (*p.p.m.*)	150	51	20·8	4·8	8·3	2·3
Exchangeable calcium (*p.p.m.*)	2,793	518	1,993	760	481	83
Exchangeable magnesium (*p.p.m.*)	492	75	162	44	69	14
Exchangeable Ca: exchangeable Mg=X:1	5·8	1·1	12·1	2·9	7·0	1·1
Total calcium (*per cent*)	1·19	0·28	0·88	0·18	0·91	0·33
Total magnesium (*per cent*)	0·545	0·066	0·511	0·066	0·548	0·047
Total Ca: total Mg=X:1	2·17	0·37	1·73	0·34	1·66	0·59
Exchangeable Ca in per cent of total Ca	25·6	10·8	24·4	13·0	6·1	2·6
Exchangeable Mg in per cent of total Mg	9·19	2·13	3·24	1·07	1·29	0·35
Exchangeable potassium (*p.p.m.*)	358	72	32	12·6	27	9·1
Exchangeable hydrogen (*m.e. 100 gm.*)	0·33	0·12	0·94	0·19	0·72	0·11
Base capacity (*m.e. 100 g.m.*)	4·67	0·29	3·82	0·61	1·63	0·06
Per cent saturation	92·9	2·8	74·1	9·6	55·5	6·1
pH	7·00	0·15	6·36	0·34	6·05	0·35
Moisture equivalent (*per cent*)	31·4	1·0	27·4	1·3	21·1	1·3
Silt[2] (*per cent*)	51·5	—	48·3	—	45·3	—
Total colloids[2] (*per cent*)	20·8	—	21·9	—	19·0	—
Clay[2] (*per cent*)	10·9	—	13·8	—	13·1	—
Fine clay[2] (*per cent*)	9·1	—	10·2	—	10·7	—

[1] Each sample was a composite of individual samples collected at 5-pace intervals on a line across the field. There were six lines, hence six samples.
[2] Composite samples from whole field.

the casts over the surrounding topsoil ranging from threefold to eleven-fold. Even the nitrogen, organic carbon, and total calcium figures are obviously highly significant, the differences being 35 to 50 per cent. The lower clay content of the casts may or may not be significant. The total magnesium contents of casts and of soil were virtually identical.

In the forest soils (Table 2) agreement among the four pro-

TABLE 2

Properties of earthworm casts and of soil from forested àreas

Profile	Casts	A1	A3	B1	Casts	A1	A3	B1	Casts	A1	A3	B1
	Total N, % (WF)[1]				Organic C, % (WF)				C:N			
I	0·630	0·382	0·133	0·086	14·9	6·5	2·0	1·3	23·8	17·1	14·7	15·7
II	0·630	0·292	0·106	0·039	17·4	5·3	1·8	0·6	27·6	18·0	17·1	15·9
III	0·717	0·320	0·151	0·071	16·6	6·8	2·7	1·0	23·1	21·1	17·5	14·7
IV	0·523	0·314	0·131	0·062	13·4	5·0	2·1	0·9	25·7	15·8	16·0	13·7
Av.	0·625	0·327	0·130	0·065	15·6	5·9	2·1	1·0	25·1	18·0	16·3	15·0
	pH				Loss on ignition, % (WF)				Available P (Truog), %			
I	5·41	4·75	4·48	4·60	27·6	13·6	5·8	4·8	27·4	22·3	7·8	9·4
II	5·35	4·65	4·55	4·69	32·4	11·7	3·6	2·9	19·4	9·1	5·1	3·9
III	5·00	4·43	4·71	4·82	30·2	12·6	5·6	3·0	21·3	20·9	6·8	13·2
IV	5.29	4·66	4·69	4·73	25·7	11·8	5·3	3·4	16·1	7·7	3·6	3·3
Av.	5·26	4·62	4·61	4·71	29·0	12·4	5·1	3·5	21·1	15·0	5·8	7·5
	Exchangeable Ca, p.p.m.				Exchangeable Mg, p.p.m.				Exch. Ca: exch. Mg= X:1			
I	4,280	1,183	95	111	328	109	27	26	13·0	10·8	3·5	4·3
II	5,300	844	151	200	511	153	24	69	10·4	5·5	6·3	2·9
III	3,272	224	51	46	354	69	15	12	9·2	3·2	3·4	3·8
IV	2,900	738	323	325	480	227	105	127	6·0	3·3	3·1	2·6
Av.	3,938	747	155	171	418	140	43	59	9·6	5·7	4·1	3·4
	Total Ca, % (WF)				Total Mg, % (WF)				Total Ca: total Mg= X:1			
I	1·00	0·94	0·62	0·59	0·378	0·648	0·614	0·580	2·64	1·45	1·01	1·02
II	1·05	0·58	0·51	0·47	0·591	0·691	0·530	0·555	1·78	0·84	0·96	0·85
III	1·40	1·46	1·36	1·21	0·592	0·643	0·564	0·580	2·36	2·27	2·41	2·09
IV	0·78	0·42	0·48	0·45	0·534	0·661	0·685	0·582	1·46	0·63	0·70	0·77
Av.	1·06	0·85	0·74	0·68	0·524	0·661	0·598	0·574	2·06	1·30	1·27	1·18
	Exch. Ca in % of total Ca				Exch. Mg in % of total Mg				Exchangeable K, p.p.m.			
I	42·8	12·6	1·5	1·9	8·68	1·68	0·44	0·45	293	217	35	35
II	42·8	12·6	1·5	1·9	8·68	1·68	0·44	0·45	293	217	35	35
III	23.4	1·5	0·4	0·4	5·98	1·07	0·27	0·21	247	115	43	25
IV	37·2	17·6	6·7	7·2	8·98	3·43	1·53	2·18	168	69	30	30
Av.	38·5	11·5	2·9	2·9	8·07	2·10	0·67	1·02	231	138	32	25

[1] *WF* values are on a water-free basis.

TABLE 2—*Continued*

Properties of earthworm casts and of soil from forested areas

Profile	Casts	A1	A3	B1	Casts	A1	A3	B1	Casts	A1	A3	B1
	Exch. H, m.e. per 100 gm.				Base capacity, m.e. per 100 gm.				% Saturation			
I	10·1	9·5	6·6	5·7	30·4	15·7	8·1	7·3	67	40	18	21
II	10·7	9·4	5·6	3·7	34·3	14·4	6·3	5·0	69	35	11	26
III	14·6	13·0	6·6	3·5	29·6	16·2	8·2	3·9	51	20	19	11
IV	10·2	9·3	5·7	4·2	27·5	13·9	7·5	5·9	63	33	24	29
Av.	11·4	10·3	6·1	4·3	30·5	15·1	7·5	5·5	63	32	18	22
	Moisture equivalent %				Total colloids, %				Clay, %			
I	48·4	27·4	19·9	19·0	13·0	13·0	6·2	25·2	8·8	8·2	5·6	14·8
II	61·2	31·2	18·5	15·4	17·8	18·0	7·8	31·6	10·0	10·8	4·0	22·0
III	49·6	26·8	18·1	12·6	21·6	24·2	13·0	32·0	12·8	15·6	6·6	21·6
IV	52·2	35·1	24·4	20·1	26·4	26·2	17·6	30·4	18·4	15·6	8·4	20·8
Av.	52·9	30·1	20·2	16·8	19·7	20·4	11·2	29·8	12·5	12·6	6·2	19·8

files was remarkably close, and differences between horizons are obviously highly significant. The higher contents of nitrogen, organic carbon, and exchangeable calcium in the casts were even more pronounced here than they were in the field soil, particularly when the A_3 horizon is considered. The A_1 and A_3 together correspond roughly to the 0–6-inch layer of the cultivated soil. On the other hand differences in available phosphorus and exchangeable potassium and magnesium were distinctly smaller than in the field soil. Total magnesium content was actually lower in the casts than in the A_1. There was no essential difference in either the total colloids or the clay content of the casts as compared with the A_1 horizon, but both were considerably lower in the A_3.

In comparison with the cultivated soil, the forest soil casts were much higher in nitrogen, carbon, exchangeable calcium, and moisture-equivalent values. The higher proportion of exchangeable calcium to exchangeable magnesium in the upper horizon of the field soil was not observed in the forest soil, nor was there any such relation between *total* calcium and *total* magnesium in either soil. The proportion of calcium that was in exchangeable form was about the same in the casts as it was in the

A_1 horizon in the field soil, but in the forest soil the proportion in the casts was distinctly higher than in the A horizons. The proportion of magnesium that was exchangeable was definitely higher in the casts in both soils.

In all cases the pH of the casts was higher than in the parent soil. Nitrate nitrogen was not determined on the forest soils. Lime applied some time in the past to the cultivated soil had raised the pH, total calcium, and, with one exception, the exchangeable calcium content of all horizons considerably above the corresponding values found in the forest soils.

DISCUSSION

Soil in which earthworms are active is invariably in better physical condition than is similar soil without earthworms. Though it is the opinion of some that the worms are present because of the favourable soil conditions, there is sufficient evidence (1, 3, 8, 10) to indicate that earthworms do very definitely improve soil structure by increasing aggregate content and porosity, thus facilitating aeration, water absorption, root penetration, and drainage. Stöckli (10) reported that casts contained no particles larger than 2 mm. in diameter and that in some cases particle size was reduced by means of a rubbing action inside the digestive tract of the worm. Mechanical analyses of our samples showed no essential differences in the texture of casts and topsoil.

From the biological standpoint, casts have been found to contain a much larger bacterial population than the unworked soil (10).

The data on chemical properties herein reported confirm those published by Powers and Bollen (5) and by Puh (6), with one notable difference in Puh's work. She found the casts to be markedly higher in total calcium but not in exchangeable calcium. No explanation for this difference was given.

Only a cursory examination of the data is needed to show the higher fertility status of the casts. What is the explanation? Is it due to substances brought up from the subsoil, or can it be attributed to direct action of the worms on the soil material?

To answer these questions, it is necessary to examine the habits of earthworms. They make their tunnels, in part, by pushing the earth away on all sides, but mostly by swallowing it and depositing the excrement at the surface. In dry or cold weather they retire to considerable depth—4 to 6 and even 8 feet. In favourable weather they are active in the top 6 or 8 inches of soil. Their food consists of plant and animal remains on the surface and in the upper layers of the soil; and apparently some nutriment is obtained from the soil itself. In the light of these facts it is interesting to speculate as to what would happen in an inverted profile, i.e., with the A and C horizons reversed. The fact that the worm casts are less acid (or less alkaline in alkaline soils) than the soil even where the worms are confined to the surface soil (6, 9), shows that the change in reaction is not dependent upon the transporting of less acid (or less alkaline) subsoil to the surface. Burrowing in the subsoil is done only to provide living quarters during unfavourable weather. It would appear, therefore, that the amount of subsoil carried to the surface is relatively small. If the subsoil is calcareous, the amount of such material brought to the surface might, over a long period of time, be sufficient to increase the calcium (and perhaps magnesium) content of the surface soil. Likewise, if the subsoil contained a higher concentration of any other material, it might influence the composition of the surface soil.

The main benefit, chemically (and biologically), of earthworm activity is the digestion of plant material and its intimate mixing with mineral soil. The concentration of the principal plant-food elements (except K) in the plant is considerably higher than it is in the soil. For example, in southern New England, forest tree leaves contain in the neighbourhood of 0·5 to 2·5 per cent N, 0·1 to 0·5 per cent P, 0·6 to 2·0 per cent K, and 1 to 4 per cent Ca; whereas the amount in the soil averages about 0·2, 0·08, 1·5, and 0·5 per cent respectively, only a fraction of which is available to the plant. Both the mechanical mixing and the action of digestive secretions favour the decomposition of the organic matter and of soil minerals. The resultant product contains a lower concentration of plant-food than the plant residues but a higher concentration than the soil. The process may be likened to the consumption of grass, hay, and grains by cattle and the subsequent return of the manure to the soil—with this difference, however. The cattle (or the milk from cows) are sold from the farm, resulting in net loss to the soil of a certain amount of plant-food. Also, some losses occur in the manure before it is incorporated with the soil. The earthworm, on the other hand, dies in the soil and its decomposed body returns plant-food to the soil without loss. It has been found that the increased nitrification that takes place when earthworms are introduced into the soil is due, in part at least, to the decomposition of their own bodies (6, 8). Russell (8) reported the nitrogen content of worms to be 1·5 to 2·0 per cent or about 10 mgm. of N per worm.

That yields may be increased by the presence of earthworms has been demonstrated in pot culture studies (5, 8). On a field scale, however, no accurate quantitative comparisons have been made, to the knowledge of the writers. Inasmuch as any practice that favours earthworm activity is also favourable to plant growth, it is extremely difficult in the field to determine to what degree the worms are responsible for any increase in yields or improvement in quality of the crop. Obviously one should avoid any practice that would materially reduce earthworm activity. Whether or not it is practicable deliberately to increase the worm population is another question and one which still lacks an answer.

SUMMARY

Samples of earthworm casts and of unworked soil from several depths were collected from a cultivated field and from four forested areas and subjected to chemical and mechanical analysis.

At the time of sampling, the field soil contained approximately three casts to the square foot, averaging 2 ounces each, or 16,000 pounds to the acre.

In the field soil, casts contained less exchangeable hydrogen and a lower clay content than the 0–6-inch layer; but the casts had higher pH values and were higher in total and nitrate nitrogen, organic matter, total and exchangeable calcium, exchangeable potassium and magnesium, available phosphorus, base

FACTS, FIGURES AND REFERENCES

capacity, base saturation, and moisture equivalent. Total magnesium was about equal in all samples.

Forest soil samples showed similar but even more striking results. Forest soil casts were higher in nitrogen, organic carbon, and exchangeable calcium, and had a higher moisture equivalent than the casts from the field soil.

These changes in composition as the result of earthworm activity are due chiefly to the intimate mixing of plant and animal remains with mineral soil in the digestive tract of the worm and to the action of digestive secretions on the mixture. That earthworms are beneficial to the soil has been established beyond a doubt. Conditions favourable to the worms, however, are at the same time favourable to plant growth, and quantitative measurements under field conditions of the part the worms play in crop production have not as yet been obtained.

REFERENCES

(1) Blanck, E., and Giescke, F. 1924. On the influence of earthworms on the physical and biological properties of the soil. *Ztschr. Pflanzenernähr. Düngung. u. Bodenk.* 3 (B): 198–210. (Abstract in *Exp. Sta. Rec.* 54:718. 1926.)

(2) Darwin, C. 1837. The formation of vegetable mould through the action of worms. *Trans. Geol. Soc.* (London) 5:505. (Also in book form: D. Appleton and Co., New York. 1882. And published by Faber and Faber, 1945, as *Darwin on Humus and the Earthworm, The Formation of Vegetable Mould through the Action of Worms.*)

(3) Hensen, V. 1882. Uber die Fruchtbarkeit des Erdbodens in ihrer Abhangigkeit von den Leistungen der in der Erdrinde lebenden Würmer. *Landw. Jahrb.* 11:661–698.

(4) Lindquist, B. 1941. Investigations of the importance of some Scandinavian earthworms for the decomposition of broadleaf litter and for the structure of mull. (In Swedish, German summary.) *Svensk. Skogsvardsför. Tidskr.* 39:179–242. (Abstract in *Biol. Abs.* D16, entry 6276.)

(5) Powers, W. L., and Bollen, W. B. 1935. The chemical and biological nature of certain forest soils. *Soil Sci.* 40:321–329.

(6) Puh, P. C. 1941. Beneficial influence of earthworms on some chemical properties of the soil. *Sci. Soc. China, Biol. Lab. Contrib., Zool. Ser.* 15:147–155.

(7) Robertson, J. D. 1936. The function of the calciferous glands of earthworms. *Jour. Exp. Biol.* 13:279–297.

(8) Russell, E. J. 1910. The effect of earthworms on soil productiveness. *Jour. Agr. Sci.* 3:246–257.

(9) Salisbury, E. J. 1924. The influence of earthworms on soil reaction and the stratification of undisturbed soils. *Jour. Linnean Soc., Bot.* 46:415–425.

(10) Stöckli, A. 1928. Studien über den Einfluss des Regenwurms auf die Beschaffenheit des Bodens. *Landw. Jahrb. Schweiz* 42:5–121.

XIV

THE NEW FRONTIER

The crowding populations of the earth stand on the last frontier
—the lands beneath their feet. Migration to more favoured
regions is no longer possible. On every border stands a man
with a gun, warning: 'You can't come here.' There is no more
land. It is is all pre-empted, with a sign erected, 'No Trespassing
—Keep Off!' Each country is determined to reserve and conserve its dwindling supply of topsoil to feed its own people.
Practically all countries in the world, particularly the more
densely populated, now face or will eventually face a need for
more arable land. There is only one possible way to supply this
pressing demand, and that is to build more soil.

We have called this last frontier a 'new frontier'—a place
of opportunity whereon we conceive of the possibility of literally
building a new earth to supply more richly all our needs and desires, both in the immediate future and for many generations to
come. The individual can exploit the potentialities of this new
frontier to his own immediate benefit. An entire nation can develop this new frontier for the present generation and for future
generations. Our concept is not based upon some magic formula
for synthetic soil-building, or speculative synthetic production
of food. Using the same tried and tested tools, forces, and
materials with which nature works, but at a highly accelerated
tempo, supplemented and aided by the use of modern machinery
and the accumulated knowledge of the forces and materials with
which we work, we can build topsoil and accomplish within a
period of months or a few short years what nature requires decades and even centuries to accomplish. Nature has provided
the example, with simple and definite instructions written into
the geological pages of the earth, in processes which we can observe, utilize, and improve upon. In the foregoing chapters of
this book we have discussed the examples and lessons which
nature has provided.

THE EARTHWORM UNDER CONTROL

As has been pointed out over and over, topsoil is the living surface of the earth upon which all life depends—both vegetable and animal life. This living surface is a very thin blanket, stretched over the earth, threadbare in many places, with vast areas of sterile rock and eroded slopes showing through. By far the greater part of earth's surface is measured in millions of square miles of non-arable land—deserts, mountains, swamps, steaming tropical jungles. The limited area of arable land has been closely estimated, surveyed, or measured.

The meaning of 'limited', as applied to the arable topsoil of the earth can be best illustrated by asking and answering two simple questions, involving rudimentary mathematics:

Question: 'How much cultivable land is there in the world?'
Answer: 'Approximately, four billion acres.'
Question: 'How many people are there in the world?'
Answer: 'Over two billion.'

That is, there is an average of about two acres of arable land per person. Consider the situation in what is probably the most favoured land in the world—the United States. With our present population, we have approximately three acres of arable land per person. Much of this land is so depleted that, commercially considered, it is hardly profitable to farm it. Of what we would call good farm land, we have approximately two acres per person. The people of the United States barely feed themselves. While we export a great deal of food, yet in normal times our imports of food practically balance exports. Were we to provide a minimum standard of nutrition, as outlined by our government experts, carefully apportioned to our entire population, there would be at all times an actual food shortage in the United States. Our lend-lease food export programme during World War II, and immediately following the war, has graphically brought to the attention of all our people the sad fact that there is not enough food to go around unless we are willing to reduce radically our standards of nutrition.

From the above, and from even a casual survey of facts and available figures, we can see that the problem of providing for our own growing population, to say nothing of the population pressure throughout the balance of the world, is immediate and pressing and not something to be considered in the distant future. Soil-conservation is not enough. In addition to conserving and increasing the productivity of the soil we have, rebuilding and conditioning our so-called 'worn out' soils and sub-marginal lands, we must build more soil on suitably located non-arable land. We have some hundreds of millions of acres of such lands on our new frontier. To exploit this new frontier, it is necessary only to apply the knowledge which we have to the available materials which we have. So far as the knowledge is concerned, we refer to the accumulated technical information of the entire world of science. For our purpose, it is necessary merely to call attention to this field of knowledge, and we can now add to it the new knowledge of atomic energy, the possibilities of which have not yet been explored for constructive use. For source materials with which to work, we briefly call attention to the mineral resources of the earth itself. Throughout the incalculable ages of the past, from the conception of primordial chaos down to the present world of form and substance as we know it, the parent mineral base of topsoil has been formed and deposited. In the superficial layers of the earth, from the visible surface on down to the bedrock, we have the inexhaustible parent mineral material of topsoil available for soil-building. The other source-parent-material of topsoil is vegetation and animal life, but primarily we should designate it as energy operating through what we popularly term 'substance' or 'material,' in the mysterious processes of life.

THE GOLD MINE IN THE SKY

Accepting gold as a symbol of value or wealth, the greatest gold mine is located in the sky. We mean the sun—figuratively speaking and literally speaking—the source of all life on this planet, earth. And from the standpoint of soil-building on the new frontier, the sun is the primary source of topsoil, and the earth is the secondary source.

Let us quote from the book *To Hold This Soil* by Russell Lord[1]: 'Blazing hot, 10,000° F. at the surface and enormously hotter

[1] Miscellaneous Publication No. 321, U.S. Department of Agriculture, under the heading of 'Celestial Dynamics'.

within, the sun is earth's immediate source of life. Most sun power goes out to other heavenly bodies or far off into space; only about one two-billionth part reaches the earth. Even so, the delivered energy averages three-eighths horse-power, day and night, on each square yard of land and sea. At noon, when the rays strike perpendicularly, the sun delivers 1½ horse-power to the square yard, upwards of 4½ million horse-power to the square mile, or 7,260 horse-power to the acre.

'Windmills run by sun-power. If the sun did not heat different parts of the earth's surface, and different layers of its water-laden atmosphere unevenly, no winds would blow. The sun draws surface water up for another run down the face of the continents. It is the pumping heart of the circulatory water system that keeps earth alive.

'Winds blow, clouds mount the wind, rain falls, and the lands are replenished. Streams and rivers flash to the sea, clouds form; and the cycle continues. "All the rivers run into the sea; yet the sea is not full; unto the place from whence the rivers come . . . they return. . . ."—Ecclesiastes 1, 7.

'Sun-power drives the weather mill that grinds soil and propels still-secret processes by which in soil, sea, leaf, and flesh, our common ingredients—sun, air, water, and a sprinkling of earthly minerals—combine into all forms of life and energy, including man.

'Our power age is a governed explosion of buried sun-power. When coal, petroleum, and gasoline are burned, they deliver energy the sun stored in plants aeons ago. Farmers ploughing, miners digging, Sunday motorists out for an airing, aeroplane drivers streaking for Europe or South America—all are developing in their various persons and from their subject beast or equipage, sun power previously fixed for use through a film of soil. . . .'

Now for the transition from the poetical statement of the abstract generalization to the more prosaic practical application and analysis of the concrete facts:

The dominant colour of the earth—what we might justifiably call the colour of life—is green. Life endures because the earth is green, the colour-evidence of the existence of a substance which has been called the most important material in the world: chlorophyll, leaf-green. Practically all the green substances of the plant world are so closely related chemically that they may, for practical purposes, be designated as leaf-green or chlorophyll. The sun, acting upon the chlorophyll in the leaf of plants through the process known as 'photosynthesis', produces sugar within the plant. And sugar is the beginning of life, the chemical start and nucleus around which the more complex compounds of protoplasm are formed. For a brief and masterly discussion of the meaning of chlorophyll, we refer the reader to a chapter in *The Green Earth*, by Harold William Rickett, under the heading of 'The Green Colour of Plants and What Comes of It'. As one simple illustration, the sunlight, acting upon the chlorophyll in 5 square inches of potato leaf, will produce about a gram of sugar per month. Quoting from *The Green Earth*, '. . . A man may use, in the same time (1 month), the sugar made by 30,000 such leaves. He may not, indeed, eat so much sugar; but all the food in his potatoes and in all the other comestibles which come to his table is derived from the sugar made in the leaves of plants—potato plants and others. A definite number of leaves whether grown in the fields or in a glasshouse, whether nourished directly by the soil or by the ingredients of soil purified and dissolved in water to make a nutrient solution—a definite area of leaf surface is necessary for the support of one man for one month.' So much for the place the sun occupies in the production of food for man. And the same nutrient elements which man uses are also used by the plant world in the growth of vegetation. The nutrition of man and all animal life is merely an incidental function of vegetation. In its entirety, we see all vegetation as a parent material of topsoil, in its eventual breaking down and disintegration recombining and mixing with the parent mineral elements of the earth to form the vital surface layer of homogenized earth.

Vegetation is bedded in topsoil. Deep into the secret, necessary darkness of the earth the roots of plants ramify, selecting the mineral elements which enter into their structure. Into the air reach the bole and branches, spreading the leaf-green surface to the sun; and, through the action of sunlight on chlorophyll, appropriating the all-pervading nutritional elements from the air. Into the structure of the plant, through the life-forces working in the necessary light of day and working in the equally necessary dark of the night and dark of the earth, are combined the nutritional elements of life in the exact proportions necessary to reproduce the plant. From the parent repository of the air come 95 per cent by weight—carbon, oxygen, hydrogen and nitrogen. From the parent repository of the earth come 5 per cent by weight—potassium, silicon, calcium, phosphorus, sodium, magnesium, sulphur, chlorine, iron, with traces of many other known elements of the universe. To provide a chemical picture of the estimated average composition of the vegetation of the earth, expressed in pounds per thousand pounds of dry matter, we will give a breakdown table of the figures. The figures are taken from *Soil and Civilization* by Milton Whitney, Chief of the Bureau of Soils, U.S. Department of Agriculture, with rearrangement for purposes of illustration.

1,000 POUNDS OF DRY VEGETATION

From air	Pounds		Food classification	
Carbon (C)	443·0	A total of 950	Protein	100 pounds
Oxygen (O)	429·0	pounds of elements	Carbohydrates	
Hydrogen (H)	61·8	derived from the		820 pounds
Nitrogen (N)	16·2	air, representing	Fats	30 pounds

From earth		
Potassium (K)	16·8	
Silicon (Si)	7·0	
Calcium (Ca)	6·2	
Phosphorus (P)	5·6	
Sodium (Na)	4·3	
Magnesium (Mg)	3·8	
Sulphur (S)	3·7	
Chlorine (Cl)	2·2	
Iron (Fe)	0·4	

A total of 50 pounds of the named mineral elements derived from the earth, all entering into or assisting in the manufacture of the above-named food materials. While we have not named other trace elements, such as Boron, which constitute a minute part of the whole, these trace elements are of tremendous importance and cannot be ignored in arriving at final conclusions. These figures have been given to illustrate and emphasize the part which the sun plays in providing, through photosynthesis, the major part by weight of parent material for the building of topsoil.

From the foregoing pages, we can see that we will have no shortage of parent materials with which to work and exploit the new and last frontier. We hear the age-old soldier-crusader cry, the eternal questioning cry of conquering man on his upward path, 'Where do we go from here?' As the idea takes hold of the constructive mind and creative imagination, the entire surface of the earth becomes a pleasant work-ground. There are no waste places: all is right and useful to the all-seeing and comprehending mind of man. The earth and the fulness thereof becomes a new earth. We see that we can spread the sun-trap of leaf-green in practically all the so-called waste places of the earth, to catch and transform the inexhaustible resources of the air into usable, soil-building material for man. The tropical jungles, with their myriad forms of quick-growing vegetation, insect and animal life, become a region for profitable harvest. The parent elements of topsoil, the parent elements of life itself, cannot elude us. We have our earth, with the roots of vegetation to search out and mine the mineral elements from it; we have our sun-trap and the sun, to catch hold of the elements from the air while we transport them to the place of ultimate use. And we have the earthworm, holding the secret of soil-building and waiting to become the servant of man in the day and hour when man needs a new servant.

As has been pointed out, any individual can harness the earthworm to build soil. Such individual use is a very simple matter. However, in the larger use of earthworms, their utilization becomes an engineering problem to be worked out by engineers. In the larger use, we can utilize standard heavy machinery, such as tractors, bulldozers, dredges, road-building machinery, compost grinding machines, shredders. Eventually all sewage and garbage disposal will become a soil-building operation, in its final stages a biological process. The waste products of the world will feed the world. The garbage of a city will be transformed into enough topsoil to produce food for the city in a recurring cycle. It is not our purpose to attempt to go into engineering details, but to indicate and point out the possibilities, based on known facts.

Throughout the ages of the past the earthworm in nature has been a master-builder of topsoil on the old frontiers. The earthworm is destined to become a master-builder of topsoil on the new frontier, harnessed and used intensively in the controlled service of man.

CONCLUSION—SUMMARY

'*Animal life in all its forms, from microbe to man, is the great transformer of vegetation into perfect earthworm food, the animal life itself, in the end, becoming food for the earthworm. In the process of transformation, a small percentage becomes animal tissue, but most of it becomes humus-building food for worms. In the feeding of domestic animals, such as cattle, sheep and pigs, out of each 100 pounds of grain fed, on the average, 89½ pounds becomes excrement, waste and gases, and 10½ pounds is represented by increase in animal weight.*

'*In a never-ending cycle untold millions of tons of the products of forest and farm, orchard and garden, are harvested, to be transformed into potential earthworm food after they have nourished animal life and served man. All the biological end-products of life —kitchen and farm waste, dead vegetation, manures, dead animal residues—constitute the abundant cheap source of earthworm food, waiting to be utilized in a profitable manner through the scientific, intensive culture of domesticated earthworms.*

'*The unseen and microscopic life of the earth beneath the soil is vastly greater than the animal life which we see above the earth as birds, beasts, and men. In fertile farm land we may find as high as 7,000 pounds of bacteria per acre in the superficial layers of topsoil, eternally gorging on the dead and living vegetable material on each other and on dead animal residues—all producing earthworm food, all becoming, in turn, earthworm food. The unseen vegetable life of the soil—algae, fungi, moulds—form an additional great tonnage of material that eventually becomes earthworm food. The living network of fine roots, so important in holding the soil in place, constitutes about one-tenth by weight of the total organic matter in the upper six inches of soil—all are eventual earthworm food. In the good black soils the organic matter—earthworm food—is represented by from 140 to as high*

148

as 600 tons of humus per acre. The earthworm will not go hungry . . .'

About the first question people ask is, 'With what do you feed earthworms?' The above quotation from former pages indicates the answer to this question. In a few comprehensive words, the answer is: 'Whatever has lived and died—both vegetable and animal—is food for earthworms.' In this discussion of earthworm food we have the key to soil-building.

In the superficial layers of earth's surface, down to the bedrock, is deposited the parent mineral material of topsoil. In the world of vegetation and animal life we have the second great parent source-material of topsoil. Stated another way, we might say that the two parent sources of topsoil are: (1) the mineral surface layers of the earth; and (2) sunlight, acting upon leaf-green (chlorophyll) to synthesize the gaseous elements from the air. Then, through life-processes—bacterial action, earthworm action, fermentation, growth, decay, etc.—the parent materials are mixed, combined and compounded into what we know as topsoil; or what Charles Darwin called 'vegetable mould'.

Nature works slowly in the production of topsoil, over periods of years, centuries, or ages. In biological soil-building, as we have termed it, we take the materials which nature has provided, with the tools and forces which we have learned to use, and speed up the processes of nature. Thus we can build topsoil when we want it, where we want it, and in whatever quantity desired. The reason we can do this is because, for all practical purposes, we have inexhaustible materials and inexhaustible forces with which to work, limited only by our visualization and use of the possibilities.

Earthworms know how to compound into topsoil the parent materials of topsoil. They are limited in numbers only by the amount of available food and we have shown that there is, from a practical standpoint, an unlimited supply of food. We know how to carry on intensive propagation to produce the necessary millions and billions of earthworms as they may be required. Each worm is a miniature 'mill' for the production of topsoil. If given a chance, each worm will consume and pass through its body every twenty-four hours a weight of soil-building material equal |to its own body weight. Considered in units of one million these tiny mills produce a tremendous tonnage of topsoil in the course of a single year.

The earthworm is a warm-blooded, air-breathing 'meat' animal. One or two head of cattle, or a few pigs or other domestic animals, will weigh a ton. The combined weight of one million mature domesticated earthworms will approximate a ton. There is no essential difference between feeding other domestic animals to produce meat and feeding earthworms for intensive production. However, while the manure of other animals becomes food for worms, the manure of worms (castings) *is* topsoil which, in turn, nurtures all life—directly, vegetable life; indirectly, all animal life through consumption of the vegetable.

An old truism states that 'A chain is as strong as its weakest link.' In the chain of life, the weakest link in nature has been the slow transition of vegetable and animal life back to the soil for use again in the eternal cycle. In nature, the earthworm has been one important element of this weakest link in the chain of life. Now, by harnessing available materials and forces for the intensive propagation and use of earthworms, we have demonstrated that we can reinforce and transform this weakest link of the chain into the strongest link.

Once we catch the vision, take hold of the principle, we can go on from there. It is just as obvious as sunlight. It does not take a scientist to utilize the principles—they are so extremely simple. Stated in a few words, the basic principles are: Compost soil-building earthworm food; add water; add worms or earthworm egg-capsules; keep wet and let nature take her course. All variations from these simple basic principles are made for convenience and efficiency, regardless of whether we work in a small way with a box or tin can, or a specially designed culture bed; or work in a larger way with carefully built compost beds, which may contain even hundreds of tons of composted source materials. In earthworm culture as in other things, results will naturally depend upon the skill and care used in following the basic principles involved.

We have written a book in an endeavour to create a mental

picture of the most important animal in the world—the earthworm. When the question is asked, 'Can I build topsoil?' the answer is 'yes'. And when the first question is followed by a second question, 'How can I do it?' the answer is 'Feed earthworms.'

INDEX

153

INDEX

INDEX

INDEX

157

INDEX

INDEX

INDEX